KU-681-034

# Contents

## 6 In the Lesson 65

## 7 Teaching the Tools of Self-Help 79

## 8 The Teacher/Student Relationship 92

## Appendix I 103

0114153

**Books are to be returned on or before
the last date below.**

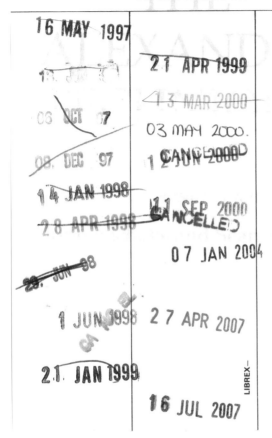

16 MAY 1997

13. JUN

06 OCT 7

08. DEC 97

14 JAN 1998

28 APR 1998

29. JUN 98

1 JUN 1998

21. JAN 1999

21 APR 1999

13 MAR 2000

03 MAY 2000.

1 2 JUN 2000 CANCELLED

11 SEP 2000 CANCELLED

07 JAN 2004

27 APR 2007

16 JUL 2007

LIBREX—

HAROLD BRIDGES LIBRARY
S. MARTIN'S COLLEGE
LANCASTER

The Brighton Alexander Training Centre

N346
995
✓ UYG D
(Nic)

0951916904

Published in Great Britain in 1991
by John Nicholls and Sean Carey

All rights reserved.

No part of this book may be reproduced, stored in a retrieval system,
or transmitted, in any form or by any means,
electronic, mechanical, photocopying, recording or otherwise
without the prior permission of the Copyright owner.

Photoset, printed and bound in Great Britain by
Redwood Press Limited
Melksham, Wiltshire

*Copies are available from:*

Dr. Sean F. Carey
4 College Terrace
Bow, London E3 5AN
United Kingdom

# Preface

This book developed out of a series of Alexander lessons that Sean Carey had with John Nicholls in 1984–85. At that time Sean Carey was a trainee teacher at Alexander Teaching Associates, Old Street, London and John Nicholls was a member of the teaching staff of the Constructive Teaching Centre, Holland Park, London.

The text represents edited and revised extracts of conversation between the two participants and focuses on two main areas: First, the context, significance and limits of the Alexander Technique and second, the problems and queries that arise from the everyday experience of Alexander teaching.

We hope that the end product will be useful since many of the questions asked by Sean Carey are those most often raised by students having lessons and by those on teacher training courses. It is emphasized, however, that neither the questions nor the answers are meant to be in any way definitive. They reflect the interests and concerns of the participants.

Nonetheless, they are an attempt to break new ground and create the conditions for dialogue and constructive criticism through which the Alexander Technique may advance.

# Preface to the Second Edition

For this second edition we have added a considerable amount of new material. Some of this deals with questions not raised in the first edition, and some goes further into questions already discussed.

The introductory section has been added so that the book would make some sense to someone who had not had lessons. We expect the book to be read mainly by teachers and trainee teachers, but we have heard from people who bought the first edition that it was read with interest by private students and even newcomers to the Technique.

We have also added the text of the 1986 STAT Annual Memorial Lecture *The Alexander Technique in a Larger Context*, since this sense of a larger context underlies the whole book.

# Acknowledgements

Some of the material in Chapter 1 previously appeared in *The Natural Family Doctor*, ed. A. Stanway, published by Gaia Books, London.

Drawings and quote from *Centred Riding* by Sally Swift on page 10 are courtesy of Heinemann.

With thanks to Lynley Culliford and Carolyn and Alison Nicholls for help with photographs and illustrations.

Thanks to Amanda Dunningham for constructive comments and material.

## Gender

To avoid awkwardness we have used the pronoun 'he' throughout in its general sense of 'he or she'.

## Terminology

We have used the term 'student' to refer to the person having lessons in the Alexander Technique, and the term 'trainee' to refer to the person engaged in training to be an Alexander teacher.

# CHAPTER 1

# The Foundation of Good Use

**SC: Could you begin our discussion by providing some basic historical information on F. Matthias Alexander?**

JN: Frederick Matthias Alexander was an Australian actor, born in 1869. Afflicted by recurrent hoarseness and breathing difficulties on stage, he set out on a patient process of self-observation over some years which led him to unexpectedly far-reaching conclusions.

What at first seemed a problem concerning *the use of his voice*, turned out to involve patterns of excessive tension and muscle pulls throughout his body, so the problem became one of *the use of his whole body*. In addition, since the very thought of projecting his voice on stage could set off these tensions, his mental approach, *the use of his mind*, was also involved. Thus, he became a pioneer of the 20th century reaction against dualism, the separation of mind and body; he preferred to talk of the 'self', including mind and body in one unit, and called the book describing his observations *The Use of the Self*.

Having found a way to solve his own problems, he soon found other actors and public speakers coming to him for help. Simply telling people how to emulate him proved inadequate however, so Alexander developed a unique form of very gentle manipulation, or, perhaps more accurately, manual guidance. He used his hands to reorganize muscle pulls in his students' bodies and so help them to better 'use of themselves'. A general improvement in health and well-being resulted, as well as improved voice and breathing. Doctors began recommending patients to him and his acting career ceased as this career of teaching flourished.

In 1904 he arrived in London, where he remained for the rest of his life. Many famous people from the theatre and public life passed, literally, through his hands, including Sir Henry Irving, Lily Langtry, Lord Lytton, Sir Stafford Cripps, G. B. Shaw,

Aldous Huxley and John Dewey (the American philosopher). However, it was not until 1931 that he felt able to train more than a handful of others to teach his technique and the Second World War interrupted the process. After his death in 1955, interest in his work waned temporarily, but in the 1970's it revived with the popularity of alternative therapies, the new body/mind disciplines from America, and the re-discovery of Eastern disciplines for body-mind integration. Some of his early trainees are still active today and running teacher-training programmes themselves.

---

'The entertainment given at the City Hall last night in which Mr. F. M. Alexander took a leading part, differed from the musical and dramatic performances which are occasionally given here, chiefly in the prominence given to the dramatic and elocutionary portions. Even the most musical among the audience, however, could not have regretted an arrangement which gave them the opportunity of listening many times during the evening to Mr. Alexander's flexible and sympathetic voice. Although – to our shame be it said – we are astonishingly backward in the proper use of our organs of speech, we are not slow to appreciate a finished elocutionist, and this Mr. Alexander undoubtedly is.'

'Mr. Alexander possesses a splendid voice, remarkable for its resonance, power and sympathy, which he uses with great taste. His scholarly style is at once apparent and the manner in which he sinks his individuality is clever.'

From newspaper reviews in Auckland, New Zealand in 1895.

---

**SC:** **I think it would be useful if you could briefly sketch what it was that Alexander discovered.**

**JN:** Basically, that all of us, when making efforts to do even the simplest things, physical or mental, impose on ourselves harmful tensions that restrict our performance. These tensions are not random but follow a definite pattern, compressing the whole body, making us actually shorter and narrower.

In the process, the column of the spine is compressed and the flexible balance of the major components of the axial column, the head, the neck and the back, is disturbed and distorted. This inter-relationship of head, neck and back was identified by Alexander as being a key factor, a 'primary control', in determining the distribution of muscle tension throughout the whole body.

Watch, for instance, someone walking towards the bus-stop, then breaking into a run as the bus rounds the corner. At that moment of extra effort, typically you will see the head drawn down towards the shoulders and the whole upper body clench downwards. Is this really a help in free breathing and movement? Observe, too, your own reactions in a tense situation, when driving, for example, or during a harassing time at work. Tight muscles pull the head down and clench the jaw; the chest is clamped, restricting breathing, and as the upper body is compressed down, the digestive organs or lower back eventually complain. Consider, finally the habitual posture of the constantly anxious or depressed person. Do you see the connection? What we popularly call posture is often the accumulated residue of all those tension reactions which have become locked into the body.

**SC: So how can people be helped to unlock these tension patterns?**

JN: In a series of Alexander lessons, the teacher will work with someone individually, one-to-one. He will use his hands to perceive chronic tensions and conflicting muscle pulls and then encourage the muscles into better balance and harmony. The touchstone of muscular harmony is that flexible balance of neck, head and back which we will look at more closely later. The student will not be required to undress; loose, comfortable clothing is fine, and there will be no forceful manipulations, as Alexander teachers do not attempt to re-position joints directly. Usually, the only equipment involved will be a firm, upright chair and a firm couch or trestle table cushioned with a blanket. The chair enables the teacher to work on the student while he is sitting and standing, and he will frequently move him from the chair to standing and vice-versa. This simple, everyday movement of standing up or sitting down is a useful tool for teaching someone to support himself and to move with less effort and tension than usual. Further work is done on the couch or table, with the student lying on his back, knees bent, feet on the table, and head slightly raised on a support.

The student's job in all this is very easy: do nothing, simply allow yourself to be guided by the teacher's hands. This is learning at a non-verbal level, by direct body experience, but the teacher will also explain over a number of lessons how you can best help yourself between lessons. This is not done by giving you special exercises to do, but by teaching you how you can consciously avoid ('inhibit' in Alexander jargon) harmful tensions, and encourage ('direct' is the jargon word) more natural posture and movement patterns to emerge.

It is a slow and gradual process. Each lesson lasts 30-45 minutes (the optimum learning time) and teachers strongly recommend having some lessons close together at first, to help you gain something of lasting value. The aim is for you eventually to become your own Alexander teacher, able, with growing awareness, to monitor your own 'use' and improve it indefinitely.

**SC: How widely available is the Alexander Technique now?**

JN: The technique is best established in the UK, where it has been known since 1904, in the USA and in Israel, where it is even used by the Israeli Air Force. There are rapidly growing numbers of teachers in the other European countries and in Australia, and a few in South American countries.By its nature and origin the Technique has had a close connection with the performing arts, and many of the great academies of music and drama employ Alexander teachers to help their students, e.g. the Royal Academy of Dramatic Art and the Royal College of Music in London and the Juilliard school in New York. Outside of such institutions, however, Alexander lessons are usually only available on a private, individual basis.

The number of teachers is growing rapidly, and there is great demand for places on teacher-training courses.

**SC: Some people would claim that the current interest in the Alexander Technique is mere self-indulgence, perhaps a legacy of the 'Me Decade' or 'New Narcissism' and not to be taken seriously. On the other hand, as long ago as 1923 Professor John Dewey called Alexander's discovery: 'as important as any principle which has ever been discovered in the domain of external nature'.[1] Equally emphatically, Dr. Wilfred Barlow wrote that the Technique is a MUST for 99% of the population.[2]**

---

[1] *Introduction to Constructive Conscious Control of the Individual* by F.M. Alexander, p. xxvi (1946 edition).

[2] *The Alexander Principle* by Dr. Wilfred Barlow, p. 20 (Gollancz 1973).

JN: I think that what journalists and social commentators describe with these labels like 'Me-Decade or 'New Narcissism' is only the surface of a much deeper movement. Over the last hundred years we in the western world have seen an urge towards greater self-awareness, self-understanding and personal responsibility for one's own behaviour, well-being and destiny.

This may seem a strange thing to say in a century which has provided unparalleled examples of mass movements and collective irresponsibility, but the two may well be linked, with the need evoking the response. It is a truism of modern times that our control over the outer world has far outstripped our control over ourselves, and I find it very helpful to view Alexander's work as part of a broad stream of development to redress that balance.

That is not, incidentally, to suggest that Alexander himself thought this way, but rather that we can now look back and see his work in a larger context.

Some important elements in that context or broad movement are:

First, the developments in psychology which began with Freud and Jung probing into the unconscious motivations behind people's behaviour. These startling revelations of how little we know of ourselves nonetheless brought with them the hope of extending our knowledge of the apparently compulsive and irrational aspects of our nature. One very important strand that arose out of psychoanalysis was the recognition by Wilhelm Reich that people's mental and emotional attitudes and behaviour had something to do with their bodies. The physical could not be separated from the psychological. The body is a manifestation or concretization of the psyche. So Reich began working with body musculature, breathing and posture, and out of that arose a whole field of body-work in psychotherapy.

Secondly, as medicine has become more and more technological, there has been a simultaneous growth of natural therapeutics. Putting the body into harmony to allow its innate self-healing forces to work is a theme common to osteopathy, chiropractic, homeopathy, acupuncture, and herbal or dietary treatments. Along with that goes an interest in making the patient more aware and responsible for himself, and an exploration of what constitutes natural functioning. In a refined and complex society, is there a way to find 'natural' diet, posture, breathing, etc?

Thirdly, it's apparent that the western world has shown increasing interest in eastern spiritual traditions, not just as philosophical ideas but as practical disciplines such as meditation, yoga and tai chi. These disciplines highlight the interdependence of mind and body and the need for greater consciousness. Gurdjieff for example, taught that people live most of their lives half asleep, acting on automatic pilot. They need to wake themselves up and greater awareness starts with being aware of your own body. Traditional Buddhist disciplines similarly stress the need for 'mindfulness,' beginning with mindfulness of physical activities and sensations. If we are to be consciously present in the moment then we must be consciously inhabiting our own bodies, not trying to be disembodied intellects.[3]

Seen within such a broad context, the relevance and importance of Alexander's work is obvious. We are out of control of our reactions and out of touch with our bodies. We are not in the driving seat of our own vehicle and not even clear what type of vehicle it is.

Conscious inhibition and direction, as described by Alexander, must be a help towards getting a foot on the brake and a hand on the steering wheel. Furthermore, the gradual unravelling of chronic physical knots that the Alexander Technique promotes, aids in bringing about what Dewey described as 'a changed emotional condition and a different outlook on life.'[4] Looked at in the broader perspective, enhanced self-awareness is a 'MUST', and the Alexander Technique is one of the most sophisticated and helpful practical aids to promoting it.

**SC:** **I wonder what type of world would it be if everyone was an exponent of the Alexander Technique?**

JN:  That's perhaps an unrealistic question because then you'd be talking about a society in which everyone was aspiring towards a high level of self-awareness. We're a long way from that. It's unlikely that a large proportion of humanity would ever have Alexander lessons. I think a large percentage of humanity may

---

[3]  This outline is greatly expanded in Appendix 1: The Alexander Technique in a Larger Context.
[4]  *Constructive Conscious Control* by F.M. Alexander p. xxii (1946 edition).

gradually attempt to find ways of helping themselves to become more conscious, but whether they'll all be flocking to the Alexander Technique is pure speculation.

SC: **I take it, then, that you don't believe that the Alexander Technique holds a monopoly of wisdom in the movement towards self-awareness?**

JN: Of course not. The technique can't claim a monopoly of wisdom and it shouldn't attempt to. That type of exclusiveness only creates opposing camps. There are invaluable and wise things in many disciplines.

SC: **To return to the question of world change, Alexander in his writings suggested the possibility of a new type of society as an extension of 'mass' good use, did he not?**

JN: We certainly can get the impression from Alexander's writings that he thought a new type of society was possible. We have to remember that his first book was written in 1910 when he was about 40 years old, perhaps 15 years after he started teaching other people. He had a missionary zeal, and understandably so. You feel from his first book, *Man's Supreme Inheritance*, particularly the first edition, this tremendous excitement and enthusiasm. He'd seen something vast, he'd seen a way of unlocking a huge area of human potential.

---

'. . . no community as yet has cultivated and developed a national consciousness in communication with reason. The psychology of nations is too large a subject to deal with here, but logically, if the principles of conscious guidance and control, as I outlined them in application to the individual, were further adopted by the nation, it is unthinkable that it should ever suffer from deterioration. It would act in all crises strictly in accordance with the dictates of reason, and guided by a judgement born of tested experience, it would be supreme.'

'The adoption of conscious guidance and control (man's supreme inheritance) must follow, and the outcome will be a race of men and women who will outstrip their ancestors in every known sphere, and enter new spheres as yet undreamt of by the great majority of the civilized people of our time. The world will then make in one century greater progress in evolution towards a real civilization than it has made in the past three.'

From *Man's Supreme Inheritance* by F.M. Alexander, pp. 149 and 155 (1957 edition).

---

However, I think it's true to say that by the time Alexander was 85 it's unlikely that he still felt he would be the midwife to a new type of society.

**SC: Do you have a working definition of the Technique?**

JN: Like many teachers, I tend to vary the description slightly according to whom I'm talking to. If someone comes for an initial Alexander lesson, it's very useful to find out why they have come and what their interests are – the problems that have motivated them to come – and then find a way of explaining the Technique that relates to what they are talking about. We'll talk about this further later on (see p. 56) but to give a definition without a specific audience in mind is difficult.

It's also difficult because the Technique seems to overlap with so many areas – it has what is called in computer jargon an 'interface' with many different processes. It has an interface with orthopaedic and osteopathic medicine, with performing art skills – how you can improve the co-ordination of a violinist for example – with the teaching of any skilled performance, with psychology and psychotherapy and with education.

**SC: And yet the impression that I get from *The Use of the Self* is that the Technique is quite simple, one is just talking about how the body – or the self – does various activities.**

JN: As soon as you introduce that phrase 'the body – or the self' you've let slip that it isn't that simple at all. You started off by saying the simple notion of 'how the body', then paused and added 'or the self – does various activities'. If it was just how the body goes about its business it would be simple, but the trouble is Alexander didn't say 'the body,' thereby recognizing the complexity of it.

So I always find it useful to look at the Technique in a broad context – within the field of these disciplines that look at the body-mind connection – and in that context one could say that Alexander work is a technique for enhancing awareness through a very precise mechanism. Now most people, if asked to be aware of their body and what they're doing with it, get a rather fragmented, piecemeal collection of sensory impressions. They'll become aware of a bit of tension in their legs, a bit of an ache in the lower back, a muzziness in the head and so on.

Frank Pierce Jones gives us an idea of what the Technique is about when in various published papers he describes it as organizing one's internal impressions around the central balance of the head, neck and trunk. The kinaesthetic perceptions are then organized around that main axis of the body, which is the key factor in posture, balance and the organization of muscle tension throughout the whole body. The balance of this central axis is, in Alexander's words, 'the primary control'. It is the key to good use, and, therefore, a remarkably good way of organizing one's kinaesthetic perceptions. In this way the organizing factor at the body level and the organizing factor at the conscious level are in harmony.

SC: **Can we define 'good use'?**

JN: We can have a go! How about this? Good use is good neuro-muscular organization, which occurs when the whole body is able to expand freely. For this to happen, the spine must be able to lengthen, which means that the neck must be free, the head going in a direction relative to the top of the spine, that is best described as 'forward and up', the muscles of the back unclenching (i.e. lengthening and widening) and the limbs functioning as extensions of the back.

There is a remarkable parallel here with the schooling of horses. Schooling is the process of training a horse to improve its conformation (outline) and co-ordination. One of the aims of schooling is to help the horse achieve what is called 'self-carriage'. This is usually defined in terms of a certain balance of the neck and head, a suppleness in the back that makes it seem long and wide, and a co-ordination of the limbs in which they seem to be functioning from the back.

Alexander called this inter-relationship of neck, head and back a primary control because when it is well-organized, as in the horse with self-carriage, we have an even distribution of muscle tone, neither sloppily relaxed nor over tense, and function better in almost every way. Through lessons we learn to avoid restricting this primary balance in ourselves (See Inhibition p. 86) and to encourage it to operate to best advantage (see Direction p. 81).

There is even a remarkable similarity between the terminology of horse-training and the terminology of the Alexander Technique. Trainers talk of how a horse 'uses itself', and, in

*Figure 1*    A Happy Horse

*Figure 2*    An Unhappy Horse

particular, how it uses its head, neck and back. How the horse uses its neck muscles to support its head, and how it coordinates that with the use of its back muscles to support the rest of its body and the weight of a rider, has for centuries been recognised as crucial to good balance and movement in a horse.[5] The equally crucial role of neck, head and back in the upright human being was not recognised until Alexander's observations. In both horse and man, the use of the neck and the use of the back are mutually interdependent; neither can be improved without attention to the other.

---

'As he does this, his neck stretches roundly from the withers [upper back] through the poll [head/neck junction], arching slightly. His jaw softens and his back widens and lengthens. His legs seem to swing smoothly and freely from his back. He looks happy.'

From *Centred Riding* by Sally Swift, p. 121 (Heinemann 1985). We, JN and SC, have added the explanatory words in brackets.

---

Incidentally, a wonderfully picturesque description of the primary control and good use was written by an enthusiastic student of the Alexander Technique, Anthony Ludovici, in 1933. In his book *Health and Education Through Self Mastery* Ludovici uses the vivid image of a bell tent in which, if the central pole is not functioning properly, the actual fabric of the tent has to be stiffened to support the whole structure. In the same way, if our central core, particularly the spinal column, is not supporting us properly, we may end up having to fix and stiffen other parts of ourselves.

SC: **All this must have an effect on breathing, too, musn't it?**

JN: It certainly does. I find it very useful when teaching to bear in mind that the Alexander Technique was first presented as a way of improving breathing. 'A new method of respiratory re-education' was F.M.'s first published description in 1907.[6]

　　　Here's an Alexander quiz question for you. Fill in the missing

---

[5] For anyone who wishes to go further into this subject, a valuable source is: *The Way to Perfect Horsemanship* by Udo Bürger (J.A. Allen 1986).

[6] See Part 3 of *Man's Supreme Inheritance*.

'But now, an order quickly given immediately put all mal-coordinations right, and then, with the automatic regularity of a man-made machine, my breath would recover its normal rhythm, my hands and arms would hang loosely from the shoulders, and I would feel my back widening and straightening, as if the slight lordosis, which I had when I first undertook the course, were visibly correcting itself.

Is it possible in a sentence to say wherein the change of conditions lay?

The nearest I can get to such a summing-up of this alteration in my stato-kinetic reflexes is to state that, whereas in the past every form of activity had been accompanied by a tendency to draw myself – my stature and my whole frame – down and in, now, by the use of my central control (primary control), I met every muscular effort by an extension of my stature and whole frame. I lengthened myself out, so to speak, at every action. To watch it (the lengthening), is to see that it is a deliberate stretch of the spine, so as to obtain a relaxation of the suspending thorax and abdomen, which allows of perfect breathing at a moment when a great effort may be necessary. Nor is the 'lengthening out' to be conceived as a marked movement. It is simply the reverse of cowering. Modern man unconsciously cowers before each effort, and by so doing imposes wholly unnecessary and often terrible strains upon his system.

While, therefore, my spine lengthened and stretched in every activity, the rest of my body – that part of it which hitherto had been stretched and tense, particularly my thoracic cage – loosened and grew mobile.

From being a tent that was supported habitually and largely by the stiffened fabric of the cloth bell, I became a tent supported by its central pole. That is the crux of the whole matter. If the reader can visualize this difference, he has visualized the change in me. For this, in fact, is what the technique achieves.

Modern men, to a far greater extent than they know, are like tents whose erect position is maintained, more or less effectively, by a stiffening of the actual fabric of the bell, instead of being maintained effectively by an irreducible pole at constant tension.

Nay, more! If the average man is watched it will be seen not only that he is like a tent trying to support itself by the stiffness of its fabric, but also that, even when he is sitting, he hangs on to everything he can – backs of chairs, tables, ledges and any projecting solid – to assist the stiffened tent wall in its abnormal task of supporting the tent.

A stiffening of the wrong parts in order to maintain erectness, however, obviously leads to all manner of faulty constrictions and strains; and it is the gradual but certain loss of these constrictions and strains, together with the transfer of the supporting strain from the fabric to the central pole, which, as one acquires the technique of correct use, constitutes at once the great benefit and the substance of the process of re-education.

Thus, as I acquired the knowledge and habit of correct use, I found that, provided my part was done – that is to say, provided I carried out my instructions and gave the correct directions for the operation of the central control (primary control) and use of my mechanisms before any activity – I was able to maintain that part of myself which hitherto had been stretched and tense in action (particularly my thoracic cage) loose and mobile, while, on the contrary, that part of myself – my tent pole, in fact – which had usually been forgotten, or if not forgotten misused (shortened, compressed, or bent), was properly brought into action to bear the principal strain of every activity.

Certain minor troubles, due chiefly to inadequate oxygenation of the blood, thus steadily improved. I distinctly grew. My clothes of a year previously were the garments of a different man. No amount of tailor's tinkering could any longer adapt them to my frame, and with it all I began to feel a new joie de vivre, a new zest both at work and at play.'

From *Health and Education through Self Mastery*, by Anthony M. Ludovici, Watts & Co., London, 1933.

---

word in the following sentence by F.M. The word refers to a particular part of the body.

'Yet it is a scientific fact that all 'physical' tension tends to cause ... rigidity.'[7]

**SC: Neck? Cervical?**

JN:  I was hoping you'd say that! No, it's 'thoracic' – rigidity in the chest. A major element in improving someone's use has to be a freeing up of the rib-cage. You could say that one half to two-thirds of the back is composed of the back of the rib-cage. The spine has to be supported in achieving its optimum length without that muscular support compromising the ability of the ribs to move laterally in breathing. And particularly to move across the back.

That brings in all sorts of considerations. Anatomical ones concerning the relationship of the ribs to the neck and back and the relationship of the diaphragm to the ribs, back and legs. Also psychophysical ones concerning the relationship of breathing to our emotional state and psychological attitudes. From traditional Indian yogic practices to modern neo-Reichian therapy, breathing has been seen as a key link between

[7] *Constructive Conscious Control of the Individual* by F.M. Alexander, p. 122 (1946 edition).

physical and psychological and between unconscious and conscious.

Figuratively it's as if the ribs are indeed a cage for most people, symbolically and physically imprisoning themselves. But undoing that cage can be a liberating and joyful experience.

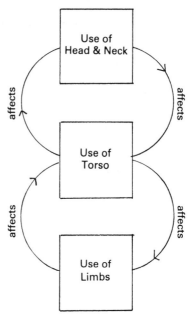

*Figure 3*    The reciprocal relationship between the use of the head and neck and the use of the rest of the body is illustrated by the sequence of F.M.'s discoveries described in *The Use of the Self*

'. . . when I succeeded in preventing the pulling back of the head, this tended indirectly to check the sucking in of breath and the depressing of the larynx.'

'. . . I came to notice that any use of my head and neck which was associated with a depressing of the larynx was also associated with a tendency to lift the chest and shorten the stature.'

'This new piece of evidence suggested that the functioning of the organs of speech was influenced by my manner of using the whole torso, and that the pulling of the head back and down was not, as I had presumed, merely a misuse of the specific parts concerned, but one that was inseparably bound up with a misuse of other mechanisms which involved the act of shortening the stature.'

'. . . it was not sufficient to put my head forward and up, but that I must put it forward and up in such a way that I prevented the lifting of the chest and simultaneously brought about a widening of the back.'

'. . . I came to see that any attempt to maintain my lengthening when reciting not only involved on my part the prevention of the wrong use of certain specific parts and the substitution of what I believed to be a better use of these parts, but that this attempt also involved my bringing into play the use of all those parts of the organism required for the activities incident to the act of reciting, such as standing, walking, using the arms or hands for gesture, interpretation etc.'

'Observation in the mirror showed me that when I was standing to recite I was using these other parts in certain wrong ways which synchronised with my wrong way of using my head and neck, larynx, vocal and breathing organs, and which involved a condition of undue muscle tension throughout my organism. I observed that this condition of undue muscle tension affected particularly the use of my legs, feet and toes . . .'

'It gradually dawned upon me that the wrong way I was using myself when I thought I was 'taking hold of the floor with my feet' was the same wrong way I was using myself when in reciting I pulled my head back, depressed my larynx etc., and that this wrong way of using myself constituted a combined wrong use of the whole of my physical-mental mechanisms.'

All quotes are from the chapter Evolution of a Technique in *The Use of the Self*, where they appear in the sequence given here.

# CHAPTER 2

# Relationship to Science and Therapy

**SC: Do you think public acceptance of the Technique has been hampered by lack of scientific research?**

JN: We need to consider what type of research would be most useful. This is a difficult question and one that faces all unorthodox therapies and techniques. You could collect thousands of case histories and they could be disputed, and dismissed as inconclusive. Besides, we don't want to be seen as providing cures for specific ailments. However, Dr. Barlow's case histories are a useful record to point to, along with his work at the Royal College of Music (London).[1] A study there in the early 1950's showed a small but measurable increase in height in students after Alexander lessons, and a reduction of tension and anxiety in performance.

In the USA many papers were published between 1955 and 1972 by Professor Frank Pierce Jones of Tufts University, Boston, showing changes in movement and muscle tension patterns after Alexander guidance.[2] Another Tufts University researcher, Dr. Richard Brown, was able to devise experiments for his doctoral thesis to show that neither suggestion nor the placebo effect play a significant role in the effectiveness of the Alexander Technique. A study at the Columbia-Presbyterian Medical Centre, New York, in 1983, showed improved breathing functions after Alexander lessons. Other studies have been published in Ph.D theses in several universities and research work is currently in progress at King's College, London, and the University of New South Wales, Australia.

**SC: A 1986 British Medical Association commission on alternative medicine asked not only for case histories and evidence of effects, but also for viable theories of how a technique works.**

[1] *More Talk of Alexander*, ch. 8 (Gollancz 1978).
[2] *Body Awareness in Action* by Frank Pierce Jones, ch. 12 (Schocken Books 1976).

**Although the Alexander Technique does not come into the category of alternative medicine, it obviously has implications for medical science. Could we provide what the BMA was asking for?**

JN:  There are certainly a number of eminent scientists who have said that Alexander's work is fully in accord with their scientific findings. They include Sir Charles Sherrington (Nobel prize winner and great pioneer of neurophysiology), Professor George Coghill (biologist), Professor Raymond Dart (anatomist and anthropologist), Professor Nikolaas Tinbergen (Nobel prize winner for his work in animal behaviour studies), and Dr. T.D.M. Roberts (author of *The Neurophysiology of Postural Mechanisms*, Butterworth, 1978).

There is an active body of knowledge derived both theoretically and experimentally around the Alexander Technique from the time that Alexander met medical and scientific people. George Coghill saw parallels between the Technique and his own work in biology and comparative anatomy on the development of movement patterns in vertebrate creatures. He focussed on the development of a small vertebrate called amblystoma, but from that and other experiments suggested that one could generalise about the development of movement in more complex creatures.

According to Coghill, this development proceeds cephalocaudally – from head to tail – in the growing vertebrate organism and the total neuromuscular patterns precede the partial ones.[3] In other words, movement of the whole body precedes the ability to move any limb or part of a limb separately. As what Coghill describes as partial patterns arise, that is, the ability to move a part such as a limb quite independently of the rest of the body, these new, local actions should normally be in harmony with the total pattern. This harmony preserves the integrity of the organism, ensuring that the functions of any one part of it do not harmfully disturb the functioning of the whole.

At this point, before quoting directly from Coghill, we should clear up a confusion in terminology. The word reflex is commonly used these days to denote a behavioural response

---

[3] Appreciation in *The Universal Constant in Living* by F.M. Alexander, p. xxii (1946 edition).

which occurs automatically on presentation of the appropriate stimulus. In the current physiological literature the term reflex often implies an innate or instinctive response, although the precise definitions given in some text books do allow for learned behaviour to become so automatic as to qualify as reflex. The language of science is sometimes not as clear and unambiguous as the popular image of science and Star Trek's Mr. Spock would have us believe. Words such as reflex, reaction and response are often used as loosely interchangeable.

Earlier in this century, the word reflex had much more strongly the implication of a learned habit, the conditioned reflex popularised by Pavlov, Watson and the behaviourists. This use of the word can sometimes be found in F.M. Alexander's books, where a harmful habit that must be re-educated may be referred to as a reflex.[4] The same use of reflex implying learned habit is found in Professor Coghill's writing. So Coghill refers to partial or local patterns as reflexes. The unwary can be led into great confusion by this one word.

So let's now look at what Coghill actually wrote. Here, in relation to walking, he says:

> 'Now the reflexes may be, and naturally are, in harmony with the total pattern, in which case they facilitate the mechanism of the total pattern (gait), or they by force of habit become more or less antagonistic to it. In the latter case they make for inefficiency in locomotion.'

And a few lines later:

> 'It is my opinion that habitual use of improper reflex mechanism in sitting, standing, and walking introduces conflict in the nervous system . . . Mr. Alexander, by relieving this conflict between the total pattern which is hereditary and innate and the reflex mechanisms which are individually cultivated, conserves the energies of the nervous system, and by doing so corrects not only postural difficulties but also many other pathological conditions that are not ordinarily recognised as postural.'[5]

One can also look at Raymond Dart who, specifically as a result of his Alexander lessons, began to speculate on the

---

[4] See, for example, pp. 26 & 27 of *The Use of the Self* (1946 edition).
[5] Appreciation in *The Universal Constant in Living* by F.M. Alexander, p. xxv (1946 edition).

underlying neurophysiological mechanisms that the Technique was affecting and through which it was having its effects. His papers on the subject are full of valuable information.[6] As the discoverer of a vital part in the fossil history of the evolution of human upright posture, and an expert in anatomy and neurophysiology, Dart was in a unique position to appreciate Alexander's work.

Frank Pierce Jones, of course, devoted many years of research to the way in which the Technique affected balance and movement and speculated about the possible mechanisms involved, particularly the attitudinal and righting reflexes. To me, his explanations now seem only partially satisfactory, but I think all Alexander teachers should read and consider them. In particular, his emphasis on the righting reflexes helps to underline the existence of self-righting processes within the human body. This in turn helps to explain why we don't have to 'do' it.

**SC: Does Dr. Roberts' book add anything to our understanding?**

JN: His book is hard going, but there is much that is relevant in Dr. Roberts' work. For example, he proposes that human upright balance is maintained by 'anticipatory, pre-emptive actions', usually supportive upthrusts, pre-empting any danger of falling. These upthrusts are aimed in a direction that is not exactly the true vertical, but the 'behavioural vertical', which is the direction required to keep your head from falling towards the ground. The precise direction required to support the head varies according to what other movements you are making, the angle of whatever support surface you are resting on, and even the tiny shifts in your own body in response to the processes of breathing and circulation.[7]

So the question 'Where is UP?' is not a trivial one. To co-ordinate the direction and magnitude of the upthrusts, our nervous system makes considerable use of sensory information from receptors in the neck. (It also, of course, requires sensory information from other sources such as the vestibular apparatus of the inner ear, the eyes and peripheral receptors in joints, skin etc.) Experiments have shown that immobilizing the neck

---

[6] Raymond A. Dart on *Skill, Poise and the Alexander Technique* (Centerline Press 1988).

[7] *The Neurophysiology of Postural Mechanisms* by T.D.M. Roberts (Butterworth 1978).

by a fixed collar, surgery or drugs seriously impairs the balance of the whole body.[8] Similarly, our own experience in the Alexander Technique suggests that if you stiffen your own neck by excessive muscle tension, you will also disturb balance throughout your body.

**SC: Where is up when there's no gravity? What happens to astronauts in outer space?**

JN: A valuable insight into this whole subject comes from the experience of American astronauts in Skylab. This was considered in a doctoral dissertation on 'Human Postural Behaviours' in 1981 by Roger Tengwall. From Skylab reports, Dr. Tengwall noted that in zero-gravity the human body folds into a semi-crouched position where limbs and head move into the mid-point of their mobility range. (Figure 4 illustrates this.)

Dr. Tengwall suggests that this observation of the body folding in on itself in zero-gravity tends to validate Alexander's thesis that the body should lengthen naturally in response to gravity.

**SC: What about the research you mentioned at the University of New South Wales and King's College, London?**

JN: In Australia, Dr. David Garlick of the University of New South Wales has been exploring the hypothesis that the Alexander Technique alters the distribution of activity in anti-gravity responses between fatiguable and non-fatiguable muscle fibres. (Because of their colour, fatiguable muscle fibre is known as white fibre, and non-fatiguable is known as red fibre.) Dr. Garlick's suggestion is that our cultural postural habit is to collapse in a heap in between bouts of strenuous exertion. This habit leads to lack of use and eventual atrophy of the non-fatiguable muscle fibres which are ideally suited to the task of ongoing postural support. Then when we do need to hold ourselves up, we have to recruit the white fibre which quickly fatigues.[9]

This hypothesis would explain why so many people say to Alexander teachers that they make attempts to have 'good posture' but soon find the process so tiring they have to collapse again. Furthermore, non-fatiguable fibre cannot be

[8]  See paper by V.C. Abrahams in *Proprioception, Posture and Emotion* ed. Dr. D. Garlick, p. 103 (University of New South Wales, Australia 1982).
[9]  *The Lost Sixth Sense* by Dr. D. Garlick (University of New South Wales, Australia, 1990).

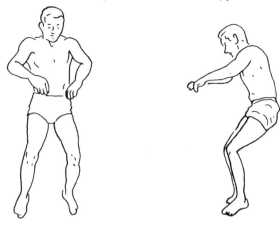

*Figure 4*   Zero-Gravity Posture

'. . . the most important deduction from these results is the validation of the 2nd discovery of F.M. Alexander and the documentation of what is frequently referred to as the anti-gravity reflex. Alexander identified this lengthening in himself by mirror observation. He replicated this many, many times with students.

The logic is as follows:
1. In gravity man stands more or less erect.
2. Without gravity man is in a 'semi-crouched' position.
3. Therefore, gravity must stimulate one or more 'lengthening reflexes' or 'anti-gravity reflexes'. (If force, or weight, were the operant factor, we would expect a 'semi-crouched' posture in the one-g environment and the more erect posture in zero g).'

From a doctoral dissertation *On Human Postural Behaviours* for the University of California (Irvine) in 1981, by Dr. Roger Tengwall.

directly controlled consciously, which may relate to why we as Alexander teachers say to our students: 'Think the directions but don't try to do them.'

**SC: And King's College, London?**

JN: Chris Stevens has been researching there, repeating some of Frank Pierce Jones' experiments with more sophisticated, up-to-date equipment, and doing other work showing the beneficial effects of Alexander lessons on blood pressure. Chris has also drawn attention to the possible role of skeletal and connective tissue structures in providing an intrinsic upthrust, a resistance to buckling which we can maximise or minimise according to our use. The combination of the curves of the spine, the intervertebral discs, the arrangement of ligaments and the active support of muscles gives the vertebral column great potential for what Chris calls 'elastic stiffness'.[10] (This may also carry through into the limbs – consider, for example, the arches of the feet.)

The spine is both a compression spring, whose stiffness can be regulated by its associated muscles, and a store of elastic energy in movements such as walking and running. In the former case, the spine's resistance to buckling means we have a built-in spring in the human body helping to take us up in response to gravity applying a load to that spring. In the latter case, the movements of arms and legs in walking and running (and dancing etc.) should reinforce each other by being amplified through the spine.

If this elastic stiffness is to function to our advantage, the muscles that support the spine in upright balance must do so without distorting the natural curves of the spine or the harmony of the ligaments, and without excessively squeezing the discs. Hence we must aim at a way of using ourselves that keeps a delicate interplay between muscles lightly bracing the vertebral column so that it is not collapsed, yet not holding the column so tightly that it cannot assert its natural resistance to buckling. Then this intrinsic springiness of the spine will in turn encourage those very same muscles that support it to ease out to their optimum length.

SC: **Is that what a teacher can sometimes feel with a hand on a student's head?**

JN: It could well be. Sometimes with a hand on the top of someone's head you can feel quite a sudden increase in firm, springy resistance to any downward pressure coming through the student's whole body, but particularly through the spine. I think that may be a moment when the student has enhanced that subtle synergy between muscles and skeleton.

SC: **So do we know the whole story, scientifically speaking, now?**

JN: In 1981, a symposium was held at the University of New South Wales, Australia, which looked at the Technique. Let me read

[10] *Inhibiting Inappropriate Habitual Postural Preparations* by Christopher Stevens. To be published in 1991.

you the summation by the Chairman, Professor A.K. McIntyre of Monash University, Melbourne:

> 'Much is now known at this simple level, and about the brain's wiring diagrams, as a result of such studies. But obviously this is totally inadequate to explain the full complexity of the central nervous mechanisms responsible for posture, locomotion, skilled movement, learning and memory, consciousness and the emotions. It is here, of course, that the holistic and observational approach of the Alexander Technique – akin to the methods of ethologists – has much to offer, despite its complete bypassing of details of the underlying neural and muscular mechanisms.
>
> 'One object of the symposium, I understand, was to examine the extent to which an adequate physiological framework can be put forward to account for the observed results of such a training, re-educative technique. How far have we succeeded in this aim? I must confess to feeling that we have not been able to make a great deal of progress. This is not really surprising, in view of the enormous complexity of the array of mechanisms involved, which even in piecemeal fashion is far from being understood: for example, even the apparently simple act of standing upright.'[11]

**SC:** **So if there is any lack of complete scientific explanation of how the Technique works, that's got a lot to do with the absence of explanations in the whole area of the neurophysiology of posture, balance and locomotion?**

JN: That's right. What we do know is that there is an anti-gravity mechanism, and that this is what we're dealing with; more specifically, we're trying to remove interferences with the efficient functioning of the co-ordination of the body that deals with upright, balanced posture – the thing that stops us subsiding into a bag of bones and organs on the ground at any one moment.

A human being doesn't stand still like a tower with each brick in perfect alignment. He is constantly moving around so there is always an interplay between the skeleton and the muscles in order to keep upright as that moving about takes place. The part of the brain that organizes this for us, and determines how

[11] *Proprioception, Posture and Emotion* ed. Dr. D. Garlick, p. 249 (University of New South Wales, Australia 1982).

much muscle tension we need to keep upright, requires information about the relative balance of the head to the body and the body to the head. Some of this information comes, of course, from that which connects the two: the neck. So we see again the primary importance of the inter-relationship of head, neck and trunk, or, more precisely, head, neck and back, since the supporting upthrusts that maintain our uprightness come mainly through the spine. This is the area we're working in, but, as I say, the whole field of posture and movement is still wide open to further scientific investigation.

Alexander liked to refer to 'the practice and theory of my Technique' instead of 'the theory and practice of my Technique'. He was very precise about that, stating that his discoveries were practical and any theory he had evolved had arisen out of practical observation. This is why the late Professor Tinbergen said the Technique was such a good example of scientific method, because it proceeded by observation, then attempted to use practical procedures to change the situation, and then observed the results. So we in the Technique see the results, even though many teachers may not be able to give a detailed theory of why they occur.

SC: **Professor Tinbergen also stated that he regarded the Technique as 'an extremely sophisticated form of rehabilitation, or rather a redeployment, of the entire muscular equipment, and through that of many other organs', and that 'many types of physiotherapy which are now in general use look surprisingly crude and restricted in their effect, and sometimes even harmful to the rest of the body.'[12] What do you think he meant by that?**

JN: It would be rash to try to guess what such an eminent man had in mind when he said that. However, one might suggest that some approaches to physiotherapy seem piecemeal in the sense that they often only deal with the part of the body that seems to be in trouble and that they usually they have a tendency to see everything in terms of muscle weakness, requiring strengthening exercises, or muscle tension, requiring relaxation exercises.

Now we say that it is impossible to take one part of the body in isolation. One would have to look at the balance of forces at

[12] *More Talk of Alexander* ed. Dr. W. Barlow, p. 254 (Gollancz 1978).

work throughout the whole musculature and if one tried to strengthen or relax one part without reference to the rest, that would be interfering with what could be called the 'ecology' of the musculature. By concentrating on one part of the body, the delicate inner mechanism which controls the appropriate degree of muscle strength and tension in all parts of the body at any one time is ignored and interfered with. This inner mechanism, as we have seen, refers particularly to the balance of the neck and head on the trunk, and can be influenced consciously to improve the situation.

SC: **No Alexander teacher would claim that the Technique is a panacea or 'cure-all' – certainly Alexander didn't. Indeed I remember you saying what we're after is improvement rather than perfection. Could you say a bit more about that?**

JN: We tend to be brainwashed by absolute concepts – right/wrong, success/failure, and so on. In dealing with the body, the muscular system, balance and movement and so on, people are prone to seeing it in terms of, 'Did I get that right?' or, 'Did I do that wrongly?,' as if there were some absolute rightness of posture or movement so that one could sign someone off and say 'Now you have achieved perfection, go away – there is nothing more for you to learn. That's it. You can now take a holiday for the rest of your life.' I think part of this attitude comes from a medical perspective which tends to be 'Either you're ill or you're cured.'

But having Alexander lessons is a process of gradually refining the mechanisms of balance, poise and neuromuscular co-ordination in everyday life. So just as in learning to sing, there are endless degrees of achievement available to people – does the person want to sing in the bath, sing folk songs at the pub or sing at Covent Garden? The same is true of the Alexander Technique. There are endless degrees in the process of self-management. That's why it's improvement rather than perfection.

SC: **Yet one Alexander teacher I know holds to an almost binary pattern of achievement – according to him either the individual is 'pulling down' or is not.**

JN: In a sense that's true, but one can then say: 'Okay, it may be true to say that either an individual is pulling down or going up' but further questions are, 'How much is the individual pulling down and how much is he going up?' That complicates the issue somewhat. Instead of being a binary system pure and simple, it's a binary system with a lot of gradations or degrees.

For example, most people are pulling down most of the time. The teacher's task is to get them to pull down rather less most of the time and, gradually, to get them to go up every now and again until eventually they go up as often as they pull down during a typical day. There might even be some days when they go up more often than they pull down. Then they're really moving forward. They're on a whole upward trend when that happens.

**SC: Is the Technique a therapy – that is, do you see it in any way as a cure for specific ailments whether 'physical' or 'psychological'?**

JN: In the broadest sense the answer is 'No' because, following Alexander, teachers of the Technique have always steered clear of presenting themselves as therapists. The reason is that the therapy approach would severely limit the scope of the Alexander Technique. It would limit it to the specific set of ailments the therapy was meant to be good for. We believe the Technique is useful for anyone. They don't have to have anything 'wrong' with them in the terms that people normally understand having something 'wrong.'

A teacher starts from the point of view that the person is an open-ended system. By that I mean that human beings are capable of a good deal more growth and development of their potential, both physical and psychological, than they normally use in an ordinary lifetime. Alexander teachers are in the business of exploring human potential. The Technique is a method by which people can make more of themselves. That's why most teachers would prefer to call it educational rather than therapeutic.

At the same time it cannot be denied that some people with particular problems do derive great benefit from the Technique. This is the territory that Dr. Barlow has explored, and rightly so, for he is a man of considerable medical qualifications and experience. It is appropriate that a medical man who has been in the Alexander Technique for so long should want to make that connection, because as Dr. Barlow points out[13] it would be quite wrong and unfair to deny the Technique to people who just wanted it to cure their back pain and say 'We're not talking to you because we're educational and not therapeutic folk.'

So all the time we have to pursue a kind of double-standard, not in a hypocritical sense but in the sense of recognizing that while we can help quite a lot of people with problems both physical and psychological, we have to make it clear to them that we are not treating them for a specific ailment but teaching them a general principle and a technique for more than just the solving of their particular problem.

SC: **Indeed! And yet we've had some teachers combining the Technique with anything from hypnotism to psychotherapy. Meanwhile, Frank Pierce Jones claimed that the Technique 'has nothing in common with the many techniques of relaxation, autosuggestion, inspirational exercise, Transcendental Meditation or mind control which catch the public fancy in one form or another.'[14] Would you agree with Jones's viewpoint or do you think he was being a bit harsh and that certain combinations are genuinely useful?**

JN: Like so many questions about the Alexander Technique one ends up giving a 'double-answer.' It seems to be important for an Alexander teacher to have 'double-vision,' especially these days when there are so many techniques which seem to be in the same area. I said earlier that the Technique interfaces with many different areas which makes it relevant to them, but it is not a part of any one of them. We have to recognize that we are part of a general movement towards self-awareness in the West in the 20th century. Yet while keeping an eye on that we also have to keep an eye on what makes us unique and distinguishes us from all those techniques that appear superficially to be similar.

Frank Pierce Jones' statement comes very much from the eye that distinguishes us as unique and I'm sure that's absolutely correct. It's very easy to watch an Alexander teacher at work, or read a bit of the literature and come away with the idea that it's a type of body work – another of these relaxation therapies, and a bit like massage – in which they get you to repeat these

---

[13] *More Talk of Alexander* ed. Dr. W. Barlow, ch. 33 (Gollancz 1978).
[14] Alexander Technique pamphlet.

instructions to yourself so there's probably a strong element of auto-suggestion too. That, I think, is to completely miss the sophistication and the subtlety of the Technique. It works on a very precise neuromuscular mechanism, or set of mechanisms, in which the systems of balance, posture, the control of muscle tension and our mental state and attitude are all intertwined and interconnected. I can think of no other technique that so clearly recognizes the interdependence of these functions.

To take a simple example: relaxation cannot be separated from how the individual organizes balance, posture and movement. That is quite unlike certain systems of relaxation and massage which proceed on a piecemeal approach – where there is an attempt to get a person to relax one bit at a time, one muscle group after another throughout the body. In the Technique we attempt to go straight to the mechanism in the neuromuscular system that determines the degree of muscle tension that is appropriate at any given time for any particular activity.

This mechanism makes judgements on the amount of muscle tension required partly on the basis of kinaesthetic information from the neck about the balance of the head on top of the trunk and the relationship of the trunk to the head. Hence the primary control is the head-neck-back relationship. This is a unique and identifying feature of the Alexander Technique and makes it a lot more powerful and sophisticated than most of the other things that Frank Pierce Jones refers to.

From the other part of our double-vision which is trying to look at the broad picture of the movement towards self-awareness, the Technique does, however, have something in common with those other things. It would be silly to deny that it helps people deal with stress more effectively. This is precisely the reason a lot of people become very keen on the Technique. They find it improves the quality of their lives as it helps them become less dragged down and burdened by stress. So the Alexander Technique is indeed connected to relaxation approaches.

When we come to look at teachers who combine the Technique with other things, there are two questions to ask: is the teacher combining the Technique with other things in the same session, such as Transcendental Meditation, hypnotherapy, massage or osteopathy? Or, is the teacher, as a qualified exponent of different disciplines, doing all these things separately?

If that's the case, he may have the same clients coming for all those things, but in different sessions.

The first situation, where the teacher mixes several things in the same session, would be undesirable to most of us because the Alexander Technique works in a very precise way. Of course, it can be very broad in its application and leaves great scope for creative thinking by the teacher in working out how to get across the fundamental principles and how to use his hands in a way that will remove interferences from the working of the natural mechanisms. Nonetheless, experience suggests that mixing things that are superficially similar but fundamentally different produces not only confusion in the student, but also, in the long run, stops the teacher from developing real skills as an Alexander teacher.

**SC: Could you spell out the practical implications of that?**

JN: For example, if someone has learned various massage techniques, or acupressure, or Feldenkrais work while training as an Alexander teacher, it will be very tempting for them, while giving an Alexander lesson, to apply these techniques when they feel areas of restriction, muscular tension and so on, instead of staying strictly with the Alexander Technique. On the face of it, this may seem a very sensible thing to do – if one has that skill then why not use it? Yet, that might well short-circuit the development of the special skills of an accomplished Alexander teacher.

The use of the hands in the Alexander way is a very difficult skill to acquire. It doesn't involve precise manipulations of the 'you put your hands here and make exactly this movement with exactly this degree of force' variety. Alexander work can look vague and ill-defined, yet there is something very precise and powerful about it in that it utilises the balance within the teacher to transmit a freeing and organising stimulus to the other person's body. If the teacher does not work at it and allows himself to take the easy option of using another skill that he already knows, he runs the risk of never acquiring the high level of skill that is potentially there. That's the danger for the teacher.

For the student, I'm afraid that type of mixing comes across as a soggy mish-mash and devalues the Technique. I'd always be wary of someone who seemed to be doing half a dozen things in one session, especially when any one of those things requires a lot of training and experience to do well.

# CHAPTER 3

# Psychology and Morality

**SC: How do you see the relationship between the Technique and psychology?**

JN: This is an important issue. A number of teachers are trained in some form of psychological counselling. These vary from the easily learned but somewhat superficial self-help techniques such as re-evaluation co-counselling to in-depth training in Freudian and Jungian approaches, gestalt therapy, psychosynthesis, bioenergetics, etc. which I think could count as more serious professional counselling skills. Once again this is an open question – let's say it's an area of future exploration. I doubt if it's possible to combine counselling of some psychological nature with Alexander work in the same session. At least that seems unlikely because the form of relationship between the student and the Alexander teacher is of a different type to that of counsellor and client.

The exploration of very emotive material might well stop the Alexander learning process by unleashing some powerful psychological forces that need to be dealt with in a skilled and subtle way. Intense emotional reactions may not be amenable to being sorted out just by the teacher's hands and a few soothing words. For that reason, it might be useful for some people to have Alexander lessons and also to devote time to counselling, or at the least to talk about the kinds of effect the Alexander lessons are having on them. This might be done with their Alexander teacher, if the teacher is properly trained in counselling skills, or it might be better for the individual to go to someone other than their Alexander teacher in order to keep the two things separate. This is an area of future experiment and exploration, but it seems important to me that the people who are going to explore it get themselves properly trained and properly qualified from reputable schools in both psychotherapy and the Alexander Technique.

Personally, I'm really put off by 'paperback psychologists'. That is, people who've read a few books and done a few short courses and think they know all the answers. Such people often have a burning desire to solve the problems of others rather than sorting out their own.

SC: **But why should psychology be useful – isn't the Technique complete in itself?**

N: The Alexander Technique is a practical tool – a practical tool that an individual can apply to his behavioural and emotional problems just as much as his physical problems. If it's applied to the emotional and behavioural problems then one enters quite complex territory and – to most people – rather unfamiliar territory. What one needs is a map or guide book to that territory. This is what psychology can provide.

For example, take someone who is having Alexander lessons and is involved in a relationship. The Alexander work will make them aware of their behaviour – it will make them aware of themselves in tense personal situations and often that means aware of feelings that may be very confusing.

It may make the person aware of anger at, or, even dislike of their partner which is very puzzling and confusing unless one has a map of the terrain and realizes that this is quite common. Such psychological mechanisms as projection and displacement, for example, are well understood by psychologists, but that type of knowledge is not yet part of the general education of most people, so for someone to become aware of such phenomena in a relationship is at first very confusing. Psychology can provide maps of patterns within our own lives and show how some of these patterns may in turn relate to patterns common to most people.

The Alexander Technique, on the other hand, is a tool that can enhance awareness of our present feelings and behaviour and can help us put psychological understanding into practice by sometimes choosing to behave differently at the moment of reaction.

Let's illustrate this with an example. Suppose a minor domestic upset leaves me feeling a surge of anger against my wife. I experience this as a particular type of 'energy charge,' blood rushing to my head, tension in my chest etc., but by endeavouring to maintain the free balance of primary neck, head and trunk inter-relationship I give myself a chance to consider how to use or release this energy. Is the anger an appropriate response to the immediate situation? If not, is the present stimulus merely a trigger for a more chronic conflict between us? Or am I re-experiencing a child-parent battle and projecting 'mother' onto my wife?

In Alexander jargon, I inhibit and direct while considering what course of action I should give consent to. Then, if it seems appropriate, free the neck – and SHOUT! If that's not appropriate, consciously let the energy charge disperse throughout the whole body by repeatedly inhibiting and releasing the tension build-up in the neck etc. and, later, come back to reconsider the situation more calmly.

Of course, if we believe in psycho-physical unity, then we also have to allow for the fact that the gradual release of chronic muscular restriction encouraged by the Technique will bring about change in the psyche. Blocked off feelings may emerge, and here also we may need to look to psychology for a map of the territory, for there is nothing in that body of knowledge called the Alexander Technique that explains how feelings can get repressed and how they can be consciously integrated when they re-emerge.

So the Technique is something that translates psychological insight into physical action. Much is done in psychology to produce insight, but we all know people who've had endless counselling and who can talk with amazing insight into their problems and motivations, but who carry on behaving very stupidly. They've failed to take that final step of translating insight into behavioural change. It's there that the Technique is so useful, but the Technique doesn't operate in a vacuum. It's up to the individual to go out and find a map to create the conditions in which real choices can be made.

In discussions like this we very easily get stuck in an either/or mode of discussion. It's understandable because all human beings tend to want THE answer. People want to say something like 'Either the Alexander Technique is THE answer or psychology is THE answer. If one is the answer, the other can't be the answer too. It's got to be one or the other.' Obviously, that's not the case. To say something has limits is not to say it's worthless and, again, to say something is useful is not to say it covers everything.

SC: I've heard some Alexander teachers claim that feelings are wholly spurious and that the best thing to do is to ignore them. On the other hand, other Alexander teachers maintain that the Technique used in such a fashion leads to a repressed personality. How do you view this issue?

JN: Some time ago Dr Robin Skynner, a well-known psychotherapist, had Alexander lessons and then gave a talk to the Society of Teachers of the Alexander Technique (STAT), London. This talk has been printed.[1] In it he states that any discipline or technique developed to liberate people from the tramlines of automatic reaction, stereotypical responses and so on, contains within itself the seeds of a subtle form of distortion or misuse whereby it can be used to avoid change – a mechanism for repression. This misuse is sometimes so close to the real, genuine use that it's very hard to detect the difference.

He ends the talk by saying that he is not going to explain what he thinks is the possible misuse of the Alexander Technique, but hints that we might look carefully at the idea of control. If one gets too concerned with control, one can be in danger of using the Technique as a mechanism for repression instead of liberation.

In talks given by Walter Carrington in his teacher training course, he makes it clear that one cannot ignore one's feelings. Alexander repeatedly writes of the need to improve one's sensory appreciation. The whole process of having lessons is in many ways the refinement of sensory awareness. One doesn't want to eradicate feelings. I mean, what lies behind motivation if it's not feelings?

The way I see it is that one of the main concerns of 20th Century Man is to re-define the relationship between conscious and unconscious processes; this was articulated by Jung, for example. Of course, some people define Alexander's notion of conscious control to mean that one has to control every thought, feeling and action. This is a recipe for insanity. It would turn anyone into a repressed automaton. It would be like the tip of the iceberg trying to control the whole of the iceberg. It is refusing to admit that there is more to oneself than the conscious mind, and if that is done, one becomes either a very sterile type of person leading a very shallow life (often

---

[1] *More Talk of Alexander* ed. Dr. W. Barlow, p. 135 (Gollancz 1978).

with a superficial air of relentless cheerfulness), or one ends up a very tight-lipped sort of Alexander teacher who is rigidly keeping everything in check. The 'I'm not going to make any spontaneous gesture without first thinking about it' variety. This is one of the dangers of the Technique and people do fall into the trap.

So it's not surprising that an outsider often complains that some Alexander teachers look stiff and rigid, but it's not meant to be so. We're not meant to try to consciously control our every thought and feeling. What we can control is how we choose to respond to those thoughts and feelings. We can do that by asking: 'Is this response going to lead to contraction and disturbance of my primary balance, or is it going to help towards expansion and maintenance of free poise?'

**SC: Could you give me a practical example?**

JN: Well, I was walking to work one morning, brooding over an argument I'd just had with someone. As we all tend to do, I was rehearsing the reasons why I was right and the other person was wrong, and the further arguments I could marshal to prove it. Gradually I became aware that my neck was stiff, my head retracted, and my ribs hardly moving so that my breathing was restricted. The irony of the situation dawned on me. I was on my way to give Alexander lessons to people – to teach them how not to do precisely those things I was now doing to myself!

As I turned my attention to directing my neck to release, my head to go forward and up, and my back to lengthen and widen, it soon became obvious that brooding on the argument was not compatible with releasing the tensions that were clamping me down and in. To restore natural balance and expansion in myself, I would have to inhibit my desire to pursue the pleasures of self-justification and resentment. This was not a matter of repressing the feeling of resentment, but rather of inhibiting my favourite response to that feeling, that of indulging in mental soap-opera. The choice was starkly clear to me: indulge, or release to regain psycho-physical integrity. There was no way to have both.

**SC: Do you think uncertainty about how to deal with emotional responses is peculiar to the Alexander world?**

JN: Not at all. The confusion and uncertainty in the Alexander
world about how to deal with emotional reactions and
problems reflects the general confusion within our whole culture about how to deal with these things. For a long time in
Northern European culture the feeling aspect of life has been
ignored and has remained unconscious. The cost of this unconscious repression has proved damaging for many people.
Some of us have tried delving into it, giving free expression to
everything; 'letting it all hang out.' The belief that the bucketful
of emotional gunge from the past that we all carry could be
emptied by catharsis ('discharge') also proved to be dangerous.
The bucket never seemed to be completely emptied, somehow
it always filled up again, and people who were engaged in that
process often became bogged down in their own seriousness
about themselves.

   Now we are looking for another way, a way of being conscious of our feelings and choosing when, where and how to
give expression to them without being at their mercy. Many
teachings, both ancient and modern, have suggested that this
can best be done from a state of 'conscious witnessing', in
which we can observe what is happening in ourselves without
being totally identified with it. To be in this state of self-observation to any sustained degree requires a great deal of free
attention and energy, more than most of us have.

   Any technique or practice that will help release attention and
energy for this process must be helpful. The Alexander Technique can help in several ways. The discipline of constantly
releasing physical tension to expand the body frees energy and
attention; the discipline of centreing consciousness in the central axis of the body, the head/neck/back, or head/spine/pelvis,
helps to keep attention in the here and now; and this centred
body-awareness cues us in to when we are going off-balance.

SC: **What then is the self? Do you see it as some sort of multi-
layered entity?**

JN: We need to avoid confusion between the term 'self,' as used by
Alexander, and 'Self,' with a capital letter, as used by some
psychologists and philosophers. Alexander means by the 'self'
the sum total of all those mechanisms of the brain, nervous
system and body that we call into play whenever we wish to act
or express ourselves in the world. The combined activity of all

the 'psycho-physical mechanisms', as he frequently refers to them in his books. In relation to this it may be interesting to look at some recent 'models':

First, the 'systems theory' viewpoint expressed most eloquently by Fritjof Capra in his book *The Turning Point* (Simon and Schuster 1982). To quote Capra: 'From the systems point of view, life is not a substance or a force, and mind is not an entity interacting with matter. Both life and mind are manifestations of the same set of systemic properties, a set of properties that represent the dynamics of self-organization.' As Capra relates, an early pioneer of this approach was American biologist George Coghill (1872–1941), who was also a keen supporter of F.M. Alexander's work. Viewed this way, all matter has an inherent drive towards self-organization, to increase the complexity of its organization, and beyond a certain threshold of complexity this can manifest as what we call 'consciousness' or 'mind'. Here the Self is simply the self organizing itself. In this model, the Alexander Technique could be said to enhance the organism's self-organizing capacity.

Secondly, the objective, scientific hypothesis of Sir Karl Popper and Sir John Eccles developed in their book *The Self and its Brain* (Springer 1977). Their view of the non-physical, conscious mind operating on a physical brain/body through 'open modules' or 'communication sites' in the higher brain would suggest a possible model for the Alexander Technique. This conscious mind (Self) could be learning to improve its communication with the brain/body mechanisms (psycho-physical self). Many might argue that this view is simply a restatement of dualism, but I have a suspicion that, as with so many philosophical arguments, the dualism/monism opposition could turn out to be a spurious one. When philosophers have battled for centuries over an issue with neither side gaining a decisive advantage, it might be time to call a truce.

Third and finally, the model commonly used in 'New Age' literature, which is a rediscovery of an ancient view, and is perhaps a more subjective model. This postulates a human being as composed of energy/matter of varying densities and vibratory rates that can be grouped in different levels – e.g. physical, emotional, mental and spiritual. It is usually postulated that there may be some integrating aspect, often called the Self or Transpersonal Self (i.e. beyond the individual personality) which is the coordinating and motivating factor in the whole system. Such a viewpoint is commonplace in alternative and complementary medicine. Looked at in this model, the Alexander Technique could be a means of enhancing conscious communication between the different levels and between all the levels and the Self.

From the point of view of any of these models we could be aspiring towards a condition (still a long way off!!!) in which the Self is more and more able to take charge of the use of the self, or better and better able to organize itself. (As Jungian psychologists would say, the centre of consciousness has shifted from the ego to the Self). Alexander wrote: 'Our endeavours should be directed to perfecting the self-consciousness of this vital essence.'[2].

The primary control is the physical level analogue of the integrating factor at all levels. To say it is an analogue means that the same principle is at work at each level, hence the esoteric teaching that awakened co-ordination of heart, throat and head chakras is a key to higher levels of consciousness and further evolution. (Heart, throat and head = upper back, neck and head). That may be why an eminent Italian psychologist said to me after his first Alexander lesson: 'This is the only bodywork that comes directly from a spiritual impulse.'

Of course, Alexander didn't speculate on these sorts of questions.

SC: **Why, because he was a pragmatic sort of chap?**

JN: Well, I think he was probably wise not to because if you are introducing a new and practical technique and, if in describing it, you bring in a lot of philosophical and metaphysical assumptions that some people may disagree with, then all those who disagree with the metaphysical assumptions will tend to dismiss the practical technique as well. Nowadays I think it must be at the discretion of individual teachers. One must remember that there are a lot of people who come to the Technique in order to play golf better, sing better, ride horses better or deal with backache. They're not interested in this speculation about consciousness. But an increasing number of people want to investigate these areas and perhaps it's time some sector of the Alexander world opened up and talked about it.

[2] *Man's Supreme Inheritance* by F.M. Alexander, p. 25 (1957 edition).

**SC:** **Do you think that good use leads, by itself, to any form of morality or ethics?**

**JN:** In the ordinary way of things, when people have private Alexander lessons, the Technique is just a tool: it does not contain within itself an explicit philosophy, religion, set of ethics, morality or anything like that. You can then use it to become better at whatever you choose to become better at. If you wish to lead a more principled or moral life according to some standard that you have set yourself, it will help you to do that. But on the other hand, if we took as an example a burglar – it seems perfectly true to say that if he wanted to become more effective at robbing other people he would indeed do so.

At a deeper level, however, one has to consider weighty statements by people like Aldous Huxley, John Dewey and Frank Pierce Jones who all seemed to believe that the Technique did lend itself to some form of ethics. Huxley writes about the Technique as a 'bridge between idealistic theory and actual practice' and as 'the psychophysical means for behaving rationally and morally.'[3] Dewey, in the introduction to *The Use of the Self*, writes of 'the great change in moral and mental attitude that takes place as proper co-ordinations are established.' These people seemed to find the Technique did lead them to behaviour that most people would describe as more moral.

**SC:** **Through what insight? Does it perhaps develop an ethic of 'Thou shalt not pull anyone else down'?**

**JN:** That's a very interesting question. One then has to explore the mechanism whereby going deeply into the Alexander Technique seems to change a person's behaviour. It's an internal thing – not 'Thou shalt not pull anyone else down,' but more 'Thou shalt not pull thyself down.' Frank Pierce Jones is the one who, perhaps, goes into the problem most clearly by talking about the growing and increasing sense of awareness of the primary control – of the balance of the head, neck and back – and how that balance and relationship is the integrating factor of the whole neuromuscular system.

Now I must confess that I read his explanation several times and for a long time I didn't understand what it meant. But as

[3] *More Talk of Alexander* ed. Dr. W. Barlow, p. 152 (Gollancz 1978).

had more experience of the Technique, I began to feel how, when the primary control is functioning in a reasonably free and uninterfered-with manner, the limbs are more integrated and coordinated with the trunk, the breathing is freer and the circulatory and digestive processes proceed unimpeded. Now that is integration on the physical level. But you also find that you feel more integrated on a psychological level and it does seem a possibility that the primary control is an indicator of integrated behaviour on both the physical and psychological levels.

A way of describing this in concrete terms is that you might find yourself in a particular social or inter-personal context where several choices of behaviour or action are open to you. If you elect to go down one of these available avenues of behaviour you might experience what Frank Pierce Jones calls 'disturbance in the tensional balance of the head on the trunk.' So at this point your own body is sending out warning signals: it's saying in effect, that this avenue of behaviour you have chosen is not doing you any good – it's creating a disturbance and disharmony in the mind and body.

At that point, you have a free choice. You can either say, 'This is not good for me. I'd better pull back from this and consider another choice of behaviour.' Or you can cheerfully say, 'I know this isn't good for me, but I like it and I'm going to do it anyway!' In no way, therefore, does the Alexander Technique impinge on free choice. It does not make moral decisions for a person – it merely sets off alarm bells that a decision has to be made, given that a particular course of action is not in the best interests of psycho-physical integration.

Developing this kind of awareness of what promotes neuromuscular harmony in yourself, and what disturbs that harmony, is a slow process, but a fascinating journey of self-study. It offers the possibility of experiencing body-mind integration in yourself more and more deeply, not as a philosophical theory but as a vividly perceived, living fact.

Of course, this leads to the question of whether there is an inherent or emergent form of morality in the Technique ? In answer to that, it needs to be said again that there is nothing in the Alexander Technique to define what sort of morality an individual should have. The Technique is not in any sense a religion or the provider of a set of moral rules.

The experience of some people who've gone deeply into the Technique suggests that it may help in the construction of a personal morality *out of one's own experience.* Of course, this perspective shares a common theme with many great spiritual traditions: that there is an inner conscience or inner guide, and that part of one's task as a human being is to come in tune – to connect – with that inner conscience or guide. So the Alexander Technique may bring out a moral guide inherent in the individual, not in the Technique itself.

---

'A more important factor is the change in moral attitude that takes place when the (Alexander) student realizes that he has within himself the power to change and control his own response patterns. One who goes on making the same fixed responses to stimuli, not because he chooses to but because he has been 'conditioned' to, has limited scope for altruistic experience. Emancipation from this kind of bondage can revive generous propensities and re-orient the outlook in the direction of altruism.

'Chiefly, however, what the Technique offers to men of good will is that it can initiate a process of psycho-physical change in which increasing awareness and increasing control reinforce each other in what might be called a 'virtuous circle.' One who understands this process can construct his own theory of altruism. He will base it not on what he has read or what he has been told about unselfishness, but upon the conscious experience of changeing selfish patterns of reaction and of observing the effects of these changes upon himself and upon others.'

Frank Pierce Jones, *Forms and Techniques of Altruistic and Spiritual Growth* ed. P.A. Sorokin, ch. 15 (Boston 1954).

---

CHAPTER 4

# Use and Misuse

SC: **Sara Barker claims in her book[1] that the Alexander Technique is a do-it-yourself technique. There are a lot of teachers who would dispute that proposition.**

N: Well, in some sense it is a D-I-Y Technique because Alexander stated that anyone could do what he did, if they did what he did. In other words, if they followed through the line of observation and reasoning that he did as described in *The Use of the Self*, then anyone would arrive at the place he did. Theoretically that is possible.

In practice, however, it seems to be very rare. Over and over again we meet people who've tried to do it from a book and quickly realized they can't – they end up feeling more stiff and awkward than they did before they tried. After all, F.M. himself wrote: 'It took me years to reach a point that can be reached in a few weeks with the aid of any experienced teacher.'[2]

SC: **What do you make, for instance, of this description by Sara Barker of what she calls 'the basic movement' in relationship to standing up?**

**'Sit in a chair of average height. Begin by becoming aware of what you do with your head and your body. Turn your head from side to side and allow it to move up and away from your body. As you become aware of the upward direction, lean forward by following your head with your body. Continue following as you lean forward until your buttocks come off the chair. As you lean forward 'upward' becomes diagonal from the chair, not skyward. As soon as your weight is on your feet, you have completed the movement.'[3]**

N: Well, what is that going to mean to somebody who already has

[1] *The Alexander Technique* by Sara Barker (Bantam 1978).
[2] *The Use of the Self* by F.M. Alexander, p. ix (1946 edition).
[3] *The Alexander Technique* by Sara Barker, p. 90 (Bantam 1978).

quite a lot of disturbance and tension in the neck and around the back and a head consistently held off balance? It's likely to mean various forms of effort to move the head away from the shoulders.

If you are running a group class and there aren't enough teachers to run around and monitor everyone, you can give out various directions such as the above and people will do all kinds of pulling and stiffening of the head and neck to try to push, pull and poke the head up to some point high above the shoulders.

No matter how many different ways it is explained, most people are so conditioned into effort and tension as a way of doing things that they cannot conceive of any other way. They do not have the experience to consider a possible way of bringing about these changes without effort and tension – in fact, by the opposite, by release of effort and tension. It's not that people are stupid. It's because we are all brought up to believe that trying harder is the way to success, and that trying involves making more tension.

Really we're trying to teach people a way of working that they may never have experienced before even in childhood, that is, the ability to do things in a non-doing way – of organizing one's co-ordination so that the body does function as a reflexly operating mechanism in response to the wishes of consciousness. So without the manual intervention of someone from outside, very few people can break out of the need for effort.

Thus the role of the Alexander teacher is to give people a new kinaesthetic experience (as F.M. repeatedly stated in his books) – to reorganize the co-ordination of the whole musculature so they get a direct feeling of this new pattern. Then, when they've experienced that regularly for themselves, there's some chance that the right pathways have been established through the nervous system.

**SC: Do some people have good use 'naturally'? I've heard some Alexander teachers claim that Mohammed Ali and Fred Astaire in their prime had good use of themselves.**

JN: There do seem to be people who have a very good balance and co-ordination although I think it would be difficult to name names. Like many Alexander teachers, I prefer not to judge by what I see. It is very difficult to assess someone just by looking at them because, for example, straightness can be mimicked quite easily. A lot of dancers can make themselves look beautifully straight and poised – and seem to have superb balance – and yet those same dancers pay frequent visits to the osteopath and physiotherapist. Ballet dancers will admit that they are often the victims of chronic back and joint problems.

There are ways of short-circuiting the process: if someone is determined to do something well and that something requires good alignment, co-ordination and balance there are ways of doing it by pulling down a great deal. Sometimes it's difficult to detect that by eye, whereas a trained hand can detect it almost instantly. With someone who has good balance and co-ordination you can put a hand on their head, neck or back, and what you feel is that the whole body musculature seems to function as one unit, where the whole of the back, for example, feels like one unified sheet of elastic which is light and easily moving as the person breathes or moves their arms and legs, rather than the feeling that the back is divided into several separate muscular areas which are almost fighting against one another – some will be gripping the bones and organs underneath far too tightly while others will appear lax.

So someone with good use has a unification of the musculature. The general over-all muscle tone is light, lively and elastic as opposed to dead, heavy and fixed. Unfortunately, that is a very rare condition. Even with many children of 4 and 5 years old, patterns of misuse have already established themselves. I have doubts whether in some of these cases the child ever had perfect use. I'm beginning to think there never was a state of perfection for some of us. The idea of the perfect child may be a myth after all.

The Alexander Technique is not about trying to turn someone into such a well coordinated person that they become an ace tennis player, piano virtuoso or tightrope walker after a series of lessons. The Technique is not going to turn the average person into a super athlete. But the naturally well coordinated person may still benefit from Alexander lessons because such people are like that unconsciously.

Our human upright poise is very easily disturbed by any form of stress, which is why small children, when they are anxious or emotionally disturbed, show it not only in their faces but in their whole body posture. Thus, if someone who has good natural balance comes under a lot of stress, that balance may be disturbed. The person may not then know how to regain it because it was unconscious in the first place. Perhaps there is an element of this in the unexpected loss of form experienced from time to time by sports performers.

One distinguishing feature of man from the animals is the upright posture and another is the level of consciousness. There seems to be some relationship between these two things. It's the attempt to bring consciousness to bear that is a specific facet of the Technique and makes it more than just a process of muscular co-ordination.

SC: **Why, then, if the eye is unreliable in assessing good use, do most books on the Alexander Technique have pictures in them illustrating good use?**

JN: Well, pictures are an excellent way of making an impact. Their real purpose is to evoke something in people – to evoke a recognition, an image, to work almost subconsciously – because apart from anything else, in a culture like ours there are so many visual images pumped at us through television, papers and magazines of what is bad use. I'm thinking for example, of the distorted use associated with glamorous, sexy, tough and powerful people. Good images that can counter that tendency are very welcome.

SC: **So if it's not possible to assess good use with the eye, is it possible to assess bad use visually?**

JN: I've heard a story of Alexander telling the students on his teacher training course that he was expecting his best student for a lesson and that they should look out for her in the waiting room. A few minutes before the lesson was due to start, all the trainees went along and peeped into the waiting room to see the best student but couldn't see her. So they came back to Alexander and said 'No, she's not there.' Alexander said, 'Yes, she is. I saw her come in.' The trainees replied, 'No, no. There's only some old woman who's all bent and stooped in the waiting room.' To which Alexander replied, 'Yes, that's her. That's my best student.'

There are many other examples, such as a student of mine of whom people might say: 'He must have poor use, he's so stooped.' His physical structure is still in bad shape, but he's applying the Technique so beautifully that he produces as much lightness and freedom as is possible within the limits of that structure as it is at the moment. Of course, gradually the structure changes and improves, but that takes a long time.

SC: **Some people would claim that the root of modern man's problems is urban society. It's still possible to hear Alexander people saying that if only we all went back to the countryside (and, indeed, some do precisely that) then we would all improve our use. That strikes me as a bit fanciful.**

JN: From what I've heard and read it seems that Alexander did not believe that a return to the country would lead to improved use. Alexander wrote that 20th century country people – farmworkers, for example – had in some ways even worse use than city dwellers.[4]

However, there may be a larger question here. In contemporary society there are people who feel that all our problems are due to civilization and that life would be much better if we went back to being primitive. It's the extreme end of the ecology movement, though I should add that most people involved in 'green' politics are not so naive. Still that strain of thought has a long history. It seems to me if we return to our broad picture of what's happening in this century and the move towards consciousness, then we would be betraying that urge if we regressed into some sort of primitive state.

Alexander's writings show that he felt very strongly about the evolution towards consciousness and man's privilege that he has arrived at the point where he can take charge of his evolution. From the perspective of depth psychology, we find equally firm views. Jung wrote: 'Since we cannot develop backwards into animal unconsciousness, there remains only the more strenuous way forwards into higher consciousness.'[5]

In a way it is a kind of blessing that we are forced by civilization to recognize that our way of life seems to be damaging us physically, because this forces us to bring consciousness to bear on the problem. It's the stimulus, the spur, to greater consciousness. So we don't want to revert to a simple primitive life

---

[4] *Man's Supreme Inheritance* by F.M. Alexander, p. 3 (1957 edition).
[5] On the *Psychology of the Unconscious* by C.G. Jung, p. 59 (Collected Works Vol. 7).

in an unconscious sense, even though a more conscious society might choose a somewhat simpler life. There are, after all, many thinkers nowadays, who talk of the emergence of a 'post-industrial society,' and are looking at the social and political structures relevant to such a society. Maybe we would have a less sedentary way of life under those circumstances. What we need to do is move forward to that, not to regress unconsciously into primitiveness.

**SC:** **Professor Nikolaas Tinbergen argues that modern man sits too much and walks too little.[6] If we accept that the sedentary life is in part responsible for our condition, what about such anti-sedentary activities as walking, jogging or aerobics?**

JN: Alexander talks about this in *Man's Supreme Inheritance* where he refers to a character called John Doe. He's in his thirties, has a high-powered office job, is under a lot of pressure and, as one might expect, starts to develop certain signs of physical and mental stress and deterioration. So he decides to take some exercise: every day he does some sort of vigorous workout and briefly feels better for it afterwards. Now he feels better for it, of course, for all the reasons that the books on aerobics state: during exercise a lot of oxygen is pumped round the blood stream. If someone stimulates their circulatory and breathing systems aerobically, it will make them feel better. It is also important to recognize that it is not going to stop the long-term and steady deterioration of what in our jargon, we would call 'use.' This will continue because John Doe is just oscillating between a sedentary job and these hard physical work-outs.

It's like being on a see-saw. It would be much more helpful if John Doe could get to the middle of the see-saw most of the time, instead of moving between one end and the other at different times. That is just moving between extremes – it's an unbalanced way of life – and John Doe is learning nothing that affects the fundamental patterns of neuromuscular organization in the body that are gradually deteriorating.

A big problem is that people think of muscles in terms of tension, relaxation, strength and weakness. They think that if their muscles are tense, they'd better relax them, or, if their muscles are weak, they'd better strengthen them. Now the

---

[6] *More Talk of Alexander* ed. Dr. W. Barlow, p. 218 (Gollancz 1978).

Alexander world considers muscles in terms of length – and that is a very different type of thing because in tensing, relaxing, strengthening and weakening, the muscle can remain at the same length.

When, however, a muscle lengthens, it is a totally different thing that is going on. It brings the muscle into a state where it is more stretched and yet more relaxed at the same time, where it is in one sense both weaker because it has had to let go to lengthen, and yet stronger because a lengthened muscle has more potential strength. It's a dimension that is outside the experience of most people because they go from tension to relaxation, from strength to weakness, and never experience the return of the muscle to its proper resting length.

SC: **So if one were to do aerobics, running and so on, then one would be much better off doing them when the muscles have been stretched?**

JN: Simple stretching is better than nothing before an aerobics session or running. It's an improvement, but it's still a long way from what we're after. The Alexander Technique is highly sophisticated in this area. It attempts to bring about a coordinated, integrated lengthening of the entire body musculature, as the postural reflexes function to evoke full height and expansion in response to gravity. There's nothing remotely like it. People can't quite grasp it. Once again, it's not because they're stupid – rather, it's because it's outside their experience.

SC: **I'd like to press you on one further topic – why aren't relaxation techniques as efficient as the Technique? Would you say that they're better than nothing, but that it's not really what we're after?**

JN: Yes. Again it's better than nothing. We all need more stillness in ourselves, that's the deepest meaning of 'inhibition' and 'non-doing' (another Alexander jargon word). Roughly, the nervous system operates in two modes: inhibitory and excitatory. Neural impulses are fired down the system which have an excitatory effect communicating that something is required to be done, or else inhibitory impulses are fired down the system communicating that there should be a stop on some action, or at least a waiting period before the action is done.

Now with most people the wiring has become very confused. It is fair to say, as Alexander did, that most people are so over-stimulated by the frenzy of modern life that they're in a constant state of over-excitation. That's why people are so jumpy, so wound up, nervous, anxious and aggressive. So, of course, everyone needs to wind down, to slow down, to come to a greater inner stillness. Anything that helps people to do that is useful.

The Alexander Technique helps people to do that in a way that is so much more sophisticated than anything else I know of. It takes into account the relationships between balance, posture, muscular tension and consciousness which are aspects that are not normally recognized as inter-related. It works, first, through the muscular system by recognizing that there is a primary control of muscular tension throughout the whole body. This means an individual does not have to come to relaxation and stillness by trying to relax every muscle in turn. Popular systems of relaxation, for example, say things like, 'Start with your left foot. Tighten the left foot and let it go. Then tighten the calf of the left leg and let it go. Then tighten the thigh of the left leg and let it go. Move to the right foot,' and so on until the person moves their way round the whole body.

None of that is necessary once it's recognized that there is a primary control. All that's necessary is to work with that: the neck is released so that the head goes out, and the back lengthens and widens. If a person puts his attention into the working of the primary control, gradually the tensions reorganize themselves throughout the body. I say the tensions reorganize themselves throughout the body rather than that the person relaxes. The individual will undoubtedly feel more relaxed because tension will have been distributed to the places where it is necessary, having been removed from the places where it is unnecessary. The beauty of this distributive process is that the individual does not have to think where it's necessary and unnecessary. All that is required is that he looks after the primary control. The subconscious brain works it all out for him.

The basic Alexander directions – the neck releasing to allow the head to go forward and up to let the back lengthen and widen – are self-checking. It is possible to impose a certain forced lengthening of the spine on yourself, to 'do' it, in

Alexander terms, but the ribs will be held so that the back cannot widen in that situation. It is also possible to 'do' a certain kind of widening, by forcibly breathing into the back and sides, but there will be a visible curling and shortening of the spine in the process. It is even conceivable that you could manage to combine these two to present a plausible facsimile of lengthening and widening, but the attempt to do that would inevitably create rigidity in the neck and lock the head on the top of the spine.

These basic directions to neck, head and back also imply that the legs and arms should be easing out of the trunk, as if the lengthening and widening of the back is spreading out through the limbs. You can easily discover by experimentally tightening your arms and legs, how that tension pulls them in towards the centre of the body and interferes with free breathing and free expansion of both back and front of the torso.[7]

For most people, unfortunately, relaxation means postural collapse and muscular flaccidity, muscles going limp. Now where it is possible to combine muscular release and postural extension, going up to the full height, and opening out so that the body is properly extended and balanced, then all the muscles return to their correct resting length. Rather than being limp and flaccid, they are toned by being stretched to their proper resting length whilst remaining very elastic. So the result is that the muscles are stretched but not tense. That is a definition of proper muscle tone. Once again this is an experience that is unfamiliar to most people – being very relaxed and yet very alert at the same time. It is a dynamic stillness reminiscent of the goal of some of the Eastern techniques such as Zen Meditation.

**SC: I assume from what you've just said that the Alexander Technique has an advantage over relaxation techniques in helping people cope with stress?**

JN: Most of us in western societies don't suffer from life-threatening situations like war, earthquakes, famine and so on, and

---

[7] For convenience and simplicity, I am subsuming under this general statement specific directions to the arms and legs that many teachers may use and F.M. wrote and talked about. For example, 'knees to go forward and away' or 'pulling to the elbows and widening across the upper parts of the arms.' (J.N.)

yet we do seem to suffer from a high degree of stress-related diseases. People say things like: 'I've got a lot of stress' or 'I've got a stress problem' almost like they say 'I've got flu' or 'I've got a cold.' They talk about stress and tension as if it were something out there that invades them from time to time.

The thing that has to be made clear about stress is that although there may be many 'stressful situations,' it's our reactions to them that are important. What creates stress in us is the way we respond to the difficulty, not the situation itself. For most people in the Western world, stress is something we do to ourselves, not something that is done to us. What we do to ourselves under stress is to produce an imbalance in ourselves both chemically and neuromuscularly. We disturb our own balance.

Therefore, we're looking for ways for people to stop doing to themselves those things that are conventionally labelled 'Stress.' Since our perspective on these things is to look at the neuromuscular reactions, let's look at the extreme example of neuromuscular reaction to stress which is the 'startle-pattern'.

The startle-pattern is a very interesting thing for Alexander teachers to examine. It's the way people react to a sudden shock and, as Frank Pierce Jones analyses, it is a wave of contraction that starts in the head and neck muscles and moves down the body.[8] The startle pattern is the very antithesis of the Alexander directions. If the directions are neck free, head to go forward and up, back to lengthen and widen and the limbs to lengthen out of the trunk, then the startle pattern is the complete opposite of that. The neck stiffens and shortens, the head pulls back and down into the back, both extensor and flexor muscles of the trunk clench and the legs tighten as if to pull the feet up off the ground.

So when that happens a person is simultaneously pulling himself down and pulling himself up. He is both ungrounded and unbalanced. It seems very likely to be the reaction of someone who's trying to stand still and run away at the same time, which obviously creates internal conflict.

The startle-pattern is a caricature of stress reaction – it's an extreme example – but the relevance of the Technique to that is that the Alexander directions are taking you as far as possible away from the startle-pattern.

[8] *Body Awareness in Action* by Frank Pierce Jones, pp. 131–133 (Schocken Books 1976).

Of course, the startle-pattern, especially if repeated enough early on in life, when the child is plastic and malleable, can become partially fixed into the nervous system and the body musculature (which are two sides of the same coin, the muscles being agents of the nervous system). Take the case of a child who's growing up with very wound-up and aggressive parents. That's likely to make the child very frightened all the time and he'll develop a constant disposition of anxiety: not just when he's in the living room with his mum and dad, but also when he's in the playground and out with his friends. Those fear reactions will become locked into his body posture in the form of the startle pattern so that he will be carrying with him all the time a tendency to contract and shorten. In neuromuscular terms, he will already be in a mild version of the startle-pattern.

So when a pattern like that becomes moulded into the body and a person starts to think of it as 'just part of my posture,' then that person has a low threshold or tolerance level to stress. If such a person later in life has Alexander lessons, his neuromuscular balance will gradually improve. The chronic postural fixations and contractions can be eased, and gradually the threshold tolerance of stress is raised.

Now of course, although this person's disposition is slowly improving over time, inevitably he sometimes meets difficult situations. The Technique comes in there because unlike relaxation therapies, as they're normally understood, the Technique is something that is used when things are happening. You don't, for example, have to go away and lie down and relax after you've faced a stressful situation. Instead, you see a stressful situation coming and you say to yourself: 'I know what's going to happen now. I'm going to stiffen my neck and pull myself down unless I'm careful.'

So then you put your attention on the process of inhibiting and directing and try to keep yourself as free and as balanced as possible while you're dealing with the difficulty, rather than saying: 'Gosh! I'll deal with this awful predicament and then I'll go off and do my meditation' or 'I'll get through this and then do my autogenic relaxation.' The Technique is a tremendous tool for relaxation in activity. By centreing your consciousness in the axis of your body and head, you use your consciousness to monitor and inhibit interferences with balance even as you go about dealing with the situation.

**SC: Is that what Dewey meant by 'thinking in activity'?**

JN: I think it is. The Technique is control in process, rather than a palliative measure in dealing with stress build-up after the problem.

Inevitably, people won't always succeed in going through stress situations without building up any muscular tension and reactions. For everyone there are always going to be situations that are just too much to handle. In those cases you just have to do the best you can and also continue inhibiting and directing afterwards as a very effective way of dispersing any accumulated tension you weren't able to release at the moment of stress.

My own perspective on stress was broadened by giving lessons to a man from the Lebanon while he was on a short visit to London. He liked the Alexander work, but he said: 'Sometimes when I drive through Beirut I come to a road block, and militia men of one faction or another point rifles and machine guns at me. At those times, prayer is all I will be able to think of, not freeing my neck.'

From my safe western haven, I was not going to argue with him.

# CHAPTER 5

# Practicalities of Teaching

**SC:** **Since Alexander's death, and even before, several sub-traditions have developed in the teaching of the Alexander Technique. Do you think these different sub-traditions are saying the same, slightly different or even quite divergent things?**

JN: It seems that if you go into this whole question, you have to recognize that, as far as the general public is concerned, most of them are saying much the same thing. When you are training to be an Alexander teacher, the differences between the schools seem enormous and terribly important. But as a teacher you sometimes find a regular student going to have lessons with another teacher who seems to work in a totally different way, and the student comes back to tell you he's had a very good lesson with the other teacher. The moral of this is that the general public doesn't always find the vast differences that we often find.

Teaching skills may vary from a minimum level which is quite gross and crudely mechanical to the most remarkably subtle and profound, but the basic principles of the Technique seem to be so powerful that students gain considerable benefit from even the minimum level of teaching. The same wide range of abilities is found in comparable professions, e.g. osteopathy and chiropractic, voice and music teachers, and teachers of sports skills etc.

In the UK we've managed to stick together in the same professional society, because we recognise that what we have in common is greater than our differences. Again, as with other professions, it's perfectly normal that there should be different approaches to the work. That's a healthy sign of growth. We don't have to agree on every detail to be professional colleagues.

**SC:** **Some people make the claim that with the passage of time, the Technique will become diluted and ultimately lost; that future teachers will become decreasingly skilful.**

JN: At present, we have a handful of top-level, highly experienced Alexander Technique teachers trained by Alexander himself.

Then there are many middle-level teachers who are very good, and a whole range of people down from there.

Now rather than interpreting that as evidence that the Technique is being diluted, I would argue that it is well to remember there was a time when the now top-level teachers only had 5 or 10 years experience. One has to ask what were they like then? I would think it highly likely that they were no better than some teachers who have 5 or 10 years experience now. We tend to forget that these top-level teachers have 40 and 50 or more years teaching experience!

Of course, one has to recognize that it takes a long time to develop into a good Alexander teacher. What looks on the face of it to be a simple skill – because there aren't any precise manipulations and what we do seems straightforward and uncomplicated – isn't at all simple because how one goes about the business of teaching offers endless scope for improvements. One can go on learning and refining that skill. That's marvellous and a cause for optimism rather than pessimism. It means that people of our generation have ahead of us two generations of teachers who can help and inspire us gradually over the years to come up to their level, by which time we should be helping and inspiring the generations below us.

There's no reason at all why the Technique should become diluted, provided we all keep learning from the generations in front of us and helping the generations behind us. It's important to have a sense of humility in order to recognize that this is a skill that you can endlessly refine and that there is no point at which you can say there is nothing more to be learned.

Your own use is your instrument and that can always be improved.

**SC: Can you say a bit more about that? Your own use is your instrument?**

JN: A remarkable aspect of the way we have been trained to use our hands in teaching the Alexander Technique is the functional interdependence of our ability to feel what's happening in the student, our own use throughout our own body, and our ability to influence the student's use for the better.

In order to have sensitive hands, we must get a coordinated expansion throughout our whole body. It is not enough to work at sensitizing the hands in isolation; their quality is a function of our use as a whole.

We may imagine that it is enough to have nice soft and open

hands. But what about the arms attached to the hands? If our arms are stiffened and shortened by the mere effort of holding them up that will restrict sensations from the hands. So we'd better get the arms well supported from the back. How do we do that? Well, by freeing the neck to let the head go forward and up, of course, and asking the back to lengthen and widen. But if we're unbalanced and bracing the legs to support ourselves, how can the back lengthen and widen to support the arms? So the teacher's whole body must be well organized in a released, directed way.

SC: **This is specifically in order to feel, to sense what's happening in the student?**

N: In most other ways of working on the body, there would be a sensing mode, 'listening hands', then an active mode in which the hands are doing something, manipulating in some way. But in good Alexander work, this distinction disappears. The sensing mode, the way of using ourselves which makes us most receptive to what's going on in the student, is also the way of using ourselves which in itself imparts a sense of direction to the student.

It's perhaps a slightly mysterious aspect of the Alexander Technique, but the expansive, releasing direction through the teacher's own body imparts a subtle tendency for that to happen in the student. While seeming mysterious, it is quite clear and palpable once you become accustomed to it. It is also scientific in the sense that any trained person can perceive it, and precise methods are available which will reliably train people to produce this effect. An experienced teacher may seem to do more in the way of imparting positive guidance to a student's body, but the foundation underlying such work must always be this quality of the hands as an extension of the teacher's whole body.

Sensory and motor, feeling and doing are united in this way of working. Lifting, moving, pushing and pulling students about without this underlying unity is only a poor imitation.

SC: **Since we are talking about psycho-physical unity, is there an attitude of mind that goes with this?**

N: I think there are attitudes that don't go with it. I think it's very difficult to bring about that kind of use in yourself as a teacher, if your attitude towards students is one of: 'You're a mess and I'm going to put you right. I'm going to put your head forward and up and stretch your back whether you like it or not.' The harshness of attitude comes through the hands and sets up antagonism or excessive passivity in the student. So also does an attitude of almost enjoying telling students what's wrong with them.

At the other extreme, if your attitude is one of: 'I'm a caring, sympathetic, warm and healing person. Tell me all your troubles while I put my sensitive hands on you to help you feel good,' you may well fall into a collapsed state without the necessary dynamic tone in your own body to convey direction to the student. Furthermore, this over-identifying kind of sympathy will leave the teacher feeling drained and burdened by students' problems.

**SC:** **In your experience, what sort of people come for Alexander lessons?**

**JN:** I'd say they fall roughly into three groups:

First, those with what one might call quasi-medical problems who come for the relief of discomfort or pain – people with back problems, stiff and sore necks, joint problems, breathing problems and so on who have not gained relief from orthodox treatments or who have simply come straight to the Technique by recommendation.

Secondly, professional performers – musicians, actors, dancers, singers – people for whom optimum balance and co-ordination is a great help in their professional life. They often come along for Alexander lessons on the same basis that a professional singer would continue to have singing lessons throughout her career, as part of a continuing process to help maintain and improve peak-level performance.

The third group, which is the growing sector of our 'market' is made up of people who come not because they are professionally involved in body use, nor because there is anything ostensibly 'wrong' with them in a sense that a doctor would diagnose. They come because they find that having Alexander lessons makes them feel better generally and helps them to deal more effectively with life's problems. They're people who want to be more responsible for their own lives and well-being.

**SC:** **In your initial interview with a student, what do you explain to them and what do you try to find out about them?**

**JN:** In a typical interview, the best place to start is to find out something about the person. This is because the Technique can be such a difficult thing to explain, and it can be explained in a number of different ways. It helps to have some idea of why someone has come, then the teacher can tailor the explanation towards that person's particular interest or problem. If someone has come because they are part of the first category of people – those with quasi-medical problems – it is also as well to know if they have some serious physical difficulties.

For example, it is useful to know if someone has had major spinal surgery before you begin work because otherwise you might find yourself thinking: 'This back feels a bit funny, I wonder what's going on here?' only later to find that the student has had two vertebrae fused together or something like that. In any case, you have to make it clear that you are not medically qualified and if people come because they want relief from some painful, physical condition, they should consult a doctor if they have not already done so.

**SC:** **To establish whether the Technique is safe for them?**

JN: No, not for that reason because the Technique is practically always safe. You see, the way we work is very gentle and so the degree of force that we use on people is so small it's most unlikely that we could ever damage anyone. Having Alexander lessons is not like someone taking up jogging at the age of 55, who is advised to have his heart checked out before beginning. No, the reason you want them to go to a doctor is to let students know you are not responsible for their physical health.

Let's take an extreme example: you do get people coming for lessons complaining of lower back pain, quite severe back pain sometimes. In a mood of casual optimism and innocence you may tell someone that it's because their back is pulled in or compressed and some lessons will soon get rid of it. Then over several lessons, the student's back gets worse and one day you hear that she has been rushed to hospital and treated for kidney stones.

This has happened, and of course, no Alexander teacher can possibly diagnose the difference between back pain caused by kidney problems and back pain that has something to do with misuse. That's where a doctor or an osteopath comes in. They can legitimately claim they have diagnostic abilities. Alexander teachers cannot make that claim. Our training does not include enough anatomy, physiology and pathology to tell the difference between the various types of back and neck pain.

But as I say, we need to know why someone has come. If we take someone with a back problem, it might be as well to state in our explanation of the Technique that in nearly all cases of back problems, people have a continuing tendency to compress and squash themselves, to 'pull down', to tighten and to tense themselves in such a way that there is more downward pressure through the spinal column than just the natural weight of the body.

This puts a greatly increased load on the spinal discs, increases the amount of wear and tear on the spinal joints, unbalances the relationship between different groups of muscles and between muscles and ligaments, and so contributes to back problems. Therefore whatever the specific back problem, if you can teach the person to literally lighten up and take some of the pressure off themselves so that the spinal column is only subject to the normal downward pull of gravity and not any extra downward pressure created by tensions and distortions, it is bound to be of benefit.

Now that would be a way of explaining the usefulness of the Technique to someone with back problems. If you get a person who is tense, nervous and depressed you might talk about the connection between psychological tension and physical or muscular tension.

For practical purposes, if someone is experiencing mental tension, there is a corresponding muscular tension in the body, so anything the teacher can do to ease muscular tension is probably going to be helpful. One of Alexander's great discoveries was that any form of muscular tension pulls, directly or indirectly, on the spinal column, and on the head balanced on the top of the spinal column, in such a way that overall height is reduced. The shape and structure of the human body is such that the central column of the spine – the spacer which keeps everything stretched out – is shortened by muscular tension. So it doesn't matter what a person's particular pattern of muscular tension is: the teacher doesn't have to analyse the particular pattern. Instead, he can say the student is shortening and that lengthening will release many of the tensions in the process.

So, in a paradoxical way, and unlike most forms of relaxation which ask the person to let go, slump or become heavy, the Alexander teacher is asking the student to relax upwards. This is much more appropriate to people's needs and is what we've already referred to as relaxation in activity. The heavy type of relaxation may well be fine in the preparation for sleep, but it's not very helpful in establishing the appropriate muscle tone for more demanding tasks.

Performers such as actors and singers are also candidates for explanation. The singer or actor is mainly concerned with breathing and vocal activities but, of course, the functions of the vocal and breathing apparatus do not take place in a vacuum. They take place within the workings of the whole body. If a singer is compressing and distorting the total musculo-skeletal framework, he cannot expect the vocal and breathing apparatus to function at the most favourable level. The Alexander teacher concerns himself not with teaching the student how to use his voice or how to breathe but with teaching how to avoid distorting the total framework in which those things operate.

Whatever explanation is given in an initial interview, it should be kept very simple. It's probably best to talk with the person for about 10 minutes in an informal, casual sort of way and then say, 'Now, in order to understand what we're talking about, I think you'll find it's much more useful if you let me work on you for a few minutes to give you the experience of how we go about teaching the Alexander Technique.'

It might be helpful if a student is nervous or anxious, or if he has been to chiropractors and osteopaths, to say something like, 'Now, what we do with our hands is a very gentle form of manual guidance. It doesn't contain any sudden manipulation. It's not our aim to get you to relax and then take you by surprise!' Usually once you've said something like that, people will readily cooperate and allow you to put a hand on them to see how things are. It's all kept simple.

At this stage you might not say much more than that it's very useful to be able to lengthen and to come up to your full height. That's a good place to begin.

It's worth also pointing out here that the amount of verbal information you can give in the first lesson, or the first few lessons, varies enormously, simply because people vary enormously in how much they can take in.

Most new teachers tend to say too much at first, trying to get everything into the first lesson, but that only confuses the student. So it's best to keep everything slow and simple even with a highly intellectual student, especially as you don't want the intellectual understanding to run far ahead of the experiential. That only adds to psycho-physical disharmony.

Exactly what you say and when you say it, you have to work out gradually for yourself. Trainee teachers ask questions like: 'When do you tell them about the neck?' and 'How do you teach inhibition?' There are no hard and fast rules about these things except that at some point you have to bring them to the student's attention.

By all means begin by adapting what more experienced teachers say, but ideally every trainee teacher should go through a process of re-inventing all the elements of the Technique for himself, discovering it in his own life, then he can teach directly from his own experience.

**SC: You talked about three categories of people who come for Alexander lessons. Do you, for example, deal with the person who has a quasi-medical problem any differently from the professional singer or the person who's come along because they feel very tense?**

JN: No. The things you say may be very different in the sense that your explanations of the Technique may be slanted in different directions, but once you get your hands on, what you do is much the same in each case.

The reason for that is when you put your hands on, you're asking yourself a few very simple questions in order to get a quick assessment of the state of that pupil: the degree to which they're going up or pulling down, the degree to which they're fixing themselves or leaving themselves free, or to put it another way, the degree to which they're expanding or contracting. You make your assessment within those parameters in order to find out where are the main interferences with natural balance or poise. Then you use your whole body as the instrument – with your arms and hands as the communication channels – to encourage those interferences to release and to allow the postural mechanisms to work to bring the person towards more expansion, more freedom and more elasticity in musculature. You are applying what Professor Raymond Dart aptly called 'inhibitional manipulations.'[1] Manipulation in the general sense of applying skilful hands, not in the narrower sense of joint manipulation, and inhibitional because the aim is to teach the student to stop disturbing his own natural poise. The aim is not to impose on him a new pattern predetermined by the teacher.

So, in this sense then, it doesn't matter whether it's a singer with a voice problem, someone with a lower back problem or someone who's tense and nervous and who wants to feel more

---

[1] Raymond A. Dart on *Skill, Poise and the Alexander Technique*, p. 51 (Centerline Press 1988).

confident. In all these cases you will find various degrees of fixation, contraction and tension which interfere with the primary control – head balance, freedom in the neck etc. This prevents the back spreading out to its full length and width and, in turn, interferes with breathing, circulation and digestion and so on. It's all the same thing. It's almost in a way pot-luck where the symptoms happen to manifest themselves – in the voice, in the back, in the breathing or in a general sense of unease.

SC: **Alexander in *The Use of the Self* claimed that given a reasonable subject, 'a temporary change to more satisfactory conditions of use can be brought about in a short space of time...'[2] What makes a reasonable subject? Moreover, are there unreasonable subjects?**

JN: Some people are undoubtedly more difficult than others. I think that often unreasonableness is in terms of attitude and manner. For example, you can get people coming to you who are quite hostile to what you're doing. So much so that sometimes you wonder why they're having lessons. On a couple of occasions I've said to someone, 'Look, if you are so disbelieving about this and you're arguing with me all the time, what are you coming for?'

It's amazing really. People are paying you and yet they may spend the whole time arguing with you and telling you the Technique can't possibly work. Sometimes you find the reason they've come is that some other member of the family has pushed them into it and there's a lot of resistance because of that. If you get people coming because someone has pushed them into it, you may sense trouble and you'd be advised early on to get them to make some decision for themselves about whether they want to come. You can make it clear to them that it's only going to work if they come because they want to and it's not going to work if they come out of a sense of obligation to 'Mum and Dad' or because 'My wife says I've got to do it.'

Another category of difficult subjects are those who are very neurotically disturbed. This condition usually goes with extreme mal-coordination and all the time you're working on them, they're constantly pulling themselves about – wriggling around and creating tremendous disturbance and tension in themselves. In Alexander jargon you'd say of such a student:

2 *The Use of the Self* by F.M. Alexander, p. 63n (1946 edition).

'This person can't leave himself alone.' He can't just sit there and let you get on with bringing about change and improvement. With such a person the teacher's main task in the first few lessons is to quieten him down. In order to bring that about, you use every means at your disposal.

You may, for example, have to ask the student to stop talking or, at least, to stop talking so much. You may also use your voice both to explain that you want him to leave everything alone and allow you to move him around, and also to calm him by your actual tone of voice. You may also quieten him down through your manner. In effect the teacher soothes the student by maintaining a centredness in himself, by directing and leaving himself alone as he's talking to the student. In this way the teacher imparts something of what he's talking about through his own example. The teacher uses his hands in a very non-doing way so the stillness in his system is transmitted to the student. This is a form of inhibition.

Also in the category of difficult subjects (through no fault of their own) are the very seriously ill and the very old. These may present extra problems. For example, if you've got a student who's already had three slipped discs and a hernia and is 75 years old, then it's obvious that it'll be more difficult than taking a 25 year old in good health. Of course, the teacher can still help the person but it will inevitably be a much harder and longer job. The student will probably be quite fixed in the body to the extent that tissue will have become calcified.

Still, to end on an optimistic note, the vast majority of people who come for lessons are reasonable subjects. That means they can leave themselves alone and allow you to proceed with the job of trying to improve their balance and co-ordination. So an experienced teacher can bring about a change to a more satisfactory level of use in a short period of time – over one lesson, for instance. It's only a temporary change, though, because you're working with the psycho-physical patterns of a lifetime.

**SC: Why is the Alexander Technique usually carried out on a one to one basis?**

JN:   That takes us into the area of faulty sensory awareness. Alexander in his teaching career was very impressed by the fact that people could not tell what was good and bad for them in psycho-physical terms. If someone has gone around for 35 years with certain patterns of muscular tension, then that's bound to feel normal. A person cannot conceive of it being otherwise. The person lacks the direct experience of things working in a different way, so every attempt at a verbal description is interpreted via the 'lens' of his sensory awareness.

This lens has been shaped by the habitual pattern of use. It's through this lens that the individual sees all attempts to improve his pattern of use, and of course, the lens follows the pattern that is there already. Hence the enormous difficulty.

For this reason Alexander wrote that an experienced teacher can take someone in a few weeks to where it took him several years to reach.[3] The role of the teacher is to intervene with his hands in order to get across the barrier of faulty sensory appreciation, to bypass the lens through which the student is looking at the situation. Something other than verbal explanation has to intervene to give the student a different experience. The way of working with the hands must have arisen very early from Alexander's realization that it was incredibly difficult to get the message across just through words. Theoretically, people could teach themselves but very few succeed. Of course, that shows the genius of Alexander in working it out in the first place when in most attempts other people needed help from someone else.

SC: **How do you see the role of group work?**

JN: This is a big question. In the Alexander world we've tended to treat this as a single question. I think the whole issue has become confused because of that. We should recognize that there are different types of group work.

First, one has to distinguish small group teaching and large class work. The latter is where the teacher takes a class of, say, 15, 20 or more students and the former is where you have something like a 1 to 5 teacher/student ratio. So, in a group of 20 students, you might have 4 teachers. In this context students can get quite a lot of individual attention.

Now that is useful in several ways. You can offer a small group teaching environment to a number of students who have already had private lessons, often for quite some time – years, perhaps – and who find it very stimulating to come along to a five day course where there are several teachers. This means that an individual student can experience the work of several different teachers which often opens a few more doors for the student. It's also an opportunity to present students with basic anatomical information using blackboards, charts, and so on

[3] *The Use of the Self* by F.M. Alexander, p. ix (1946 edition).

which is more efficient than trying to slip in bits and pieces during a lesson.

Group teaching is also useful in giving introductory courses, perhaps in an area of the country where there aren't any Alexander teachers but where people have expressed interest. In this way people can get an experience of the Alexander Technique, to know that it brings about change in the neuromuscular system and isn't just a set of abstract ideas. This can be done in either week-long or even weekend courses.

One spin-off of this approach is that it often stimulates enough interest for a teacher to go and work in an area full-time, because people who've been given a taste of the Technique may then want to proceed by taking private lessons. I might also add here that one advantage of a group introduction is that some people are frightened of coming for private lessons. There's something about the intimacy of a one-to-one situation that frightens them until they find out a bit more about the process, so it is valuable that the group option should be available.

There's a third type of group that's not been tried much, but might be useful. That is one which serves as a forum for people who are having private lessons to come along and share their experience. Many students find they're a little bit isolated – the Alexander teacher might well be the only other person in the world who talks about the Technique with them. So it could be very useful to give those people the chance to meet others who are having lessons, particularly if the Technique is having quite profound effects on them, in order to provide time and space where they can talk, ask questions, learn from each other, get feedback from an experienced teacher and so on. These sessions could well take place on something like a monthly basis.

Finally, to go back to the large class environment where there is only one teacher and 15, 20 or more students. I should point out that this was never done in Britain until there was a demand for it from adult education institutes. It wasn't something that Alexander teachers here spontaneously invented. The result was that there were attempts to put something together that would fit into the format of an adult education class. The experience of most teachers suggests that a class situation is only useful at an introductory level – almost as a PR exercise – and it has to be made clear to people that without private lessons they're not going to proceed very far. Still, it does allow the Technique to be introduced to people who, perhaps, can't have private lessons for financial reasons.

# CHAPTER 6

# In the Lesson

**SC: What type of learning environment do you try to create in a private lesson?**

JN: The teacher's first consideration when someone comes along for private lessons is to create a sense of confidence and trust, because most people don't learn very well if they're feeling anxious and insecure. So it's part of the teacher's job as a professional to be sufficiently skilful at dealing with people to put them at ease, to make them feel at home. The whole learning process will then be much easier and pleasanter for both parties. Another important aspect of the learning environment is for the teacher to get across to the student that what they're involved in is a cooperative enterprise. It is not a test of the student's ability so students don't need to feel that every time they come for an Alexander lesson they're being put to the test. But neither is a lesson a situation where the student can feel that he can ignore his body and go off and have a little daydream while the teacher does it all for him, because it's not all going to be done for him. A lesson is a cooperative enterprise and the sooner that is established the better.

**SC: Some Alexander teachers claim the traditional form of a lesson using a chair and a table is 'old hat' and what is now required is a modern, 'dynamic' approach more relevant to everyday life.**

JN: Well, the people I've come across who advocate the modern-dynamic-approach often don't know how to use the table and the chair properly and I think they should learn how to do that before they revolutionise everything. I think that attitude often betrays a superficial understanding of the Technique, and a misunderstanding of the role of the chair and table work; in particular, the use of the chair.

If one assumes the purpose of working with someone in a chair in an Alexander lesson is to teach them how to sit down

Nine month old baby, prior to walking, and an Alexander trainee.

and stand up, then of course it would be possible to say that this is 'old hat' and we need a more adventurous format. That would be reasonable because teaching someone how to sit down and stand up is trivial and would soon become boring and, for people who prefer to sit on the floor, quite irrelevant. To view the purpose of the chair that way is a very limited view of the situation. The chair is a useful device in the process of bringing about an improvement in the student's whole balance and co-ordination.

SC: **But why this particular movement of sitting to standing and vice versa?**

JN: It is an especially useful movement in which to learn inhibition and direction because it involves the co-ordination of the muscles of the neck, the back and the legs. That is, all those muscles that are concerned with supporting us against gravity. It helps to programme into our nervous system a pattern of neck unclenched so that the head is freely poised, back lengthening and widening to support the trunk, and legs active yet not stiffened at the joints of ankle, knee and hip. These directions are programmed in a very clear way by the action of the movement itself – head and knees opposing each other so that the back stays back and expands between them. This highlights the antagonistic pulls and counter balances throughout the body that we require for good use in all movements, and the experience usually carries over quite easily into other simple movements such as walking.

But there is a further aspect to this. It is not so much overt movement that we are concerned with, as the pre-movement, or primary movement of the body's response to gravity, the lengthening upthrust that maintains our upright balance. This coordinated expansion as a response to gravity is something we all learned as babies, in the first year or two of life. Consider how the baby develops. It learns first to use its neck muscles to support its own head, then to sit upright, using its back muscles to support its trunk. From there it goes on to crawling (an activity that some teacher-training schools have found useful), and to kneeling and squatting. Already the co-ordination of the legs with the neck and back is developing. The baby will then spend some time, perhaps months, learning to come up from squatting to fully upright, at first holding on to things for support, then unsupported. This period before walking begins is one in which the baby continually rehearses the movement from squatting to standing and back again, extending and flexing the legs and often stopping part-way in the flexed attitude we call 'monkey'. As balance becomes more reliable, there will even be the occasional venture up onto the toes, usually with great delight.

With this picture of child development in mind, the classic Alexander lesson with the chair takes on new significance. We are recapitulating the learning of balanced, upright sitting, and trying to go from there to full extension of the limbs without disturbing the balance of head, neck and trunk. We are, in the same process, recapitulating a part of the up and down between squatting and standing the baby repeatedly practices.

Going down to full squat is difficult for many adults and less convenient for the teacher. With the addition of the monkey attitude, which is any position intermediate between full squat and fully upright, and going up on the toes, we could reasonably claim to be guiding our students consciously to repeat the early learning process that develops the anti-gravity responses of upright balance. This time, because the student is learning more consciously, he has a chance to inhibit and undo interference patterns developed during or since the early learning process.

The movement is secondary. It's getting the experience of expansion and allowing the primary control to function in the activity of going up against gravity that is the paramount consideration. The further movement of sitting down or standing up is secondary to dealing with gravity. You have to recognise, therefore, that as a teacher you are there not just to show people how to sit down and stand up, nor how to do other things directly like how to walk, climb stairs, sit at a desk and write, or pick up shopping bags. That is not the teacher's main purpose. The teacher is there to unlock the deep patterns of contraction that have become built into what is popularly called 'posture', to unlock those chronic patterns of tension, and thus free the natural mechanisms of posture and balance. One might even say the teacher is there to help the student find 'natural' balance, posture and movement by the removal of those chronic interferences.

In this sense, inhibition and non-doing are indeed the foundation of the Technique and the foundation of good teaching. You are not there to 'do' something to your students, nor are you there to teach them to 'do' something. It is essentially an 'undoing' process.

So how someone walks, climbs stairs, picks up shopping bags and so on will improve as a result of the freeing of the natural mechanisms. Once it is understood that the teacher and the student are working at this deep level, then the chair and the table are all that are required. There's endless scope for improving and refining our use of ourselves within this simple context.

SC: **I think nearly everyone who has been involved with mainstream Alexander work over a period of time has at least some**

experience of that lengthening upthrust, the primary movement you just mentioned. Yet there are some teachers who
claim that all this emphasis on going up, on antagonistic pulls
and counterbalances, is misguided and invariably leads to a
lot of stiffening. They claim that what teachers ought to show
their students is simply how to move with the head leading
and the body following, or how to release into a free-flowing,
multi-dimensional openness.

JN: The statement that 'The head leads and the body follows' is
often bandied around in Alexander circles, but it needs a bit of
looking at. It comes from Magnus' research on animals, usually
decerebrate, and Magnus himself was uncertain at first
whether his observations applied to normal human adults. He
did later decide his work indeed applied to humans as well, but
the subject is not a simple one.

In a four-legged animal it's fairly obvious its head normally
goes first and its body follows because it's oriented along a
horizontal axis. Our spines point upwards along a vertical axis,
so how does our head lead us? Well, obviously not in a gross
way. Not by having to deliberately move our head before we
move any other part of ourselves.

In terms of that primary movement of upward lengthening
against gravity, the head cannot lead in the sense of supplying
the motive power for upward lengthening. Despite images of
helium-filled balloons, the head is not lighter-than-air, and
despite images of sky-hooks, there are no muscles hanging
from convenient clouds to catch passing heads and give them a
lift. The head can certainly go forward, because it is unevenly
balanced on top of the spine with more of its weight in front of
the spine than behind it. But it can only go up by virtue of what
happens underneath it. The motive power, the energy that
takes the head up must be the activity of the body below it. The
head can only go up by being carried up by the combined action
of the extensor muscles of the neck, back and legs, the inherent
springiness of the skeletal and connective tissue structures
(intervertebral discs, spinal curves etc.), and everything else
that provides our uniquely human uprightness. It rides
upwards on the elevator of the rest of the body.

Freeing the neck to let the head go forward is necessary to
unlock the motive power and to ensure it is steered in the most

appropriate direction, but the power comes from the whole body.

---

'I discussed the following statement with Alexander himself and he was in complete agreement about its validity: "The head goes forward by its own weight, and up by the concerted activity of the anti-gravity musculature of the body" '.
   From the transcript of an unpublished talk by Walter Carrington to his training course, 5th June 1972.

---

Of course this brings us back to the value of chair work and procedures such as monkey, which are building up the co-ordination of neck, back and legs that takes us up. And encouraging the widening which frees the ribs, especially at the back, and therefore supports the lengthening and ensures it is not forced.

If we think rather crudely that the Alexander Technique is simply a matter of letting the weight of our head stretch our spines in every movement we make, we can easily encourage a forward and down drag throughout ourselves. This will certainly be different to our previous way of using ourselves, and may feel more relaxed, but it's not forward and up.

SC: **Yes. My own experience of that kind of work is that it leaves me feeling free, loose and floppy, but certainly not up. After lessons with good mainstream teachers I often feel a powerful sense of up flowing throughout myself, which is extremely pleasurable, and it's as if my head acts as the mechanism for steering that upgoing self into activity.**

JN: Indeed. I think it's really in that sense of steering the upward energy that the head leads. The sensory receptors of the skull (vestibular apparatus) and of the neck being so important in establishing the direction of 'up'.

SC: **Could all this emphasis on an upward direction have an un-grounding effect on some people?**

JN: Oh, it could do if you're not clear about it. Any kind of straining up can have an ungrounding effect, physically giving a sense of not being firmly supported on the ground, and psychologically a sense of insecurity. That's why it's so helpful to appreciate that there are natural anti-gravity, self-righting processes in the human body. We can go up naturally in response to gravity. We don't have to 'do' it. We simply have to ask it to happen and avoid the ways of using ourselves that prevent it from happening.

Release in the legs and hips is an essential part of this, since we must allow the effects of gravity to flow through us in order to evoke the appropriate response. When we experience 'up' as a natural response to gravity, then we will feel grounded, supported by the earth, not bracing as if to bootstrap ourselves upwards.

Trainee teachers ask sometimes: 'How can I learn to help a student experience that?' The answer, of course, has to be that first and foremost it's got to be happening at least to some extent in you, the teacher. This is one of the reasons why in the training of teachers we emphasize the use and understanding of 'monkey'. Properly understood, monkey involves a freeing of the legs out of the lower back, and this must be maintained while the arms and hands are being used to work on the student. At first, this may seem very difficult, because the unconscious habit in most of us is to brace the legs and clench them into the back when attempting to do anything with the arms and hands. In the process we unground ourselves and will communicate that ungroundedness and corresponding tension to the student we are working on. If we can overcome this habit and release out through the legs to the ground while working, then that grounded expansiveness in ourselves will be communicated to the student.

SC: **When do you choose to use the chair and the table? What are the relative advantages and disadvantages of each?**

N: The chair is useful because the teacher has to deal with the problems that the student has in balancing and supporting himself in the gravitational field. How he uses his anti-gravity mechanism, how he supports and coordinates himself against gravity. When someone is lying down they're not doing very much so the teacher doesn't have the opportunity to perceive a student's particular use patterns as clearly as he can when working in the upright position with the chair. The table, however, does have the advantage that people can often let go and undo more readily than they would when standing; with the table supporting them, they are relieved of the necessity o balancing and supporting themselves. They can then let th teacher work to bring about changes with no fear of loss o balance, or worries about support.

Another particular advantage of table work from the teach er's point of view is that it's possible to work more directly on a student's legs, hips and pelvis than is possible with the person standing up. So you might well lie a person down if you thought that it would get some undoing through the student', legs.

A further reason for putting people on the table might be jus to quieten them down if they're very nervous or agitated. You see sometimes it might be very difficult to get through with the hands. Some students may be so nervous and agitated tha they cannot leave themselves alone and thus be winding them selves up all the time the teacher is trying to unwind them Lying down might settle the student more easily. I find i useful, for example, if someone comes in late for a lesson and i feeling terribly harassed, to put him straight on the table to giv him an opportunity to unwind as quickly as possible. In gen eral, however, I think it is true to say that most experience teachers prefer to start the lesson with the chair because it i possible to rapidly assess just what state the person is in b feeling the student's neck, the whole of their back and movin them in and out of the chair. In this way you can check thei co-ordination patterns very easily in the first minute or two of lesson. Once you have a clear picture of the state of a studen it's possible to put him on the table if you wish.

It's very tempting for newly qualified teachers to spend al their time working on the table because it's easier for th teacher to do table work. There's no harm in that to begin with so long as it's recognized that it's easier and that sooner or late the difficult bit – the chair work – has to be tackled. I think it' wise for newly qualified teachers to discipline themselves to d some chair work in a lesson, otherwise they're likely to fall int the habit of becoming expert at table work but never masterin the more difficult task of working in the chair. Incidentally there's no harm at all in the teacher lying people down if th teacher himself is getting tired; perhaps a few minutes wor around the table can help the teacher organize his energy a bi better.

**C:** I knew one teacher who didn't use the table very much because he reckoned lying people down resulted in a net loss rather than a net gain in muscle tone and that what most people required was the latter rather than the former.

**N:** I don't think you can say that most people lack muscle tone. I would say that most people have too much muscle tension. That's true of students who, at first sight, seem just floppy and collapsed. You often find in such cases that there are deep tensions holding such students, pulling them down, rather than everything being a totally passive collapse throughout the system. Of course, there are people whose problem is passive collapse but I think they are a very small minority.

Having said that, I don't necessarily think that every lesson has to involve a period of lying down as a matter of course. You tend to find that the better you get as a teacher, the less inclined you are to lie people down. That seems to be Walter Carrington's experience for instance. He rarely lays people down after the first few lessons. Alexander didn't seem to put people on the table very much but then he got his students to go to other teachers for what he called 'lying down work'. Generally, it's not something you can make firm rules about.

It's something that each teacher has to decide for himself. If a teacher can get all he wants through chair work then he may never have to lie anyone down except to show them how to lie down for themselves. I'd say that's unlikely, though, because there may always be people who are much taller and much heavier than you, people who are so unwieldy that the teacher does not have the size and the strength to cope with them in the chair for a whole lesson.

**C:** Do you have a set routine in teaching or does it vary considerably with each individual?

**N:** Well of course a very common routine is that a lesson begins with some chair work, then moves on to table work and then moves back to the chair. If someone watched a typical Alexander teacher doing a typical day's work, it might seem as if the teacher is doing the same thing with every person. It would probably look like an extremely routine set of procedures. The student comes in and the teacher puts a hand on their neck and a hand on their back or front, sits them down and then takes a

shoulder, stands them up again, has his hands round their
middle and then sits them down and stands them up once
more, puts them on the table and takes the head, shoulders and
legs before bringing the pupil back to the chair where the
process repeats itself.

Just think, if someone sees that with ten students, one after
another, they'll think it's absolutely routine, and yet, although
outwardly the format is very much the same from one student
to the next, the more experienced and sensitive you get as a
teacher the more it seems that you are doing quite different
things because the experience of each person under your hands
is different. As a teacher, you are, in effect, holding under your
hands a complex pattern of muscular networks and each stu
dent has a different pattern, so although the hands appear to be
in the same places, the teacher's perception of what's going on
is quite different. You're always trying to find ways of un
locking the pattern of tension in each student by applying your
own energies in slightly different areas and directions.

**SC: Why is the Alexander lesson normally 30 to 40 minutes in
length?**

JN: I suppose the 30 minute lesson was something Alexander
arrived at through practical experience. I believe he used to say
that if you couldn't get something useful happening in 30
minutes, you wouldn't get it in 45 or 50 minutes, but should
leave it and hope something would happen the next time. Here
you can see the parallels with the psychology of learning in
general. For example, the reason that most schools in this
country have lessons of 40 minutes is because that seems to be a
good learning period. If a teacher goes on too long, people stop
paying attention and quit learning. That's true whether it is an
intellectual activity or one involving a physical skill – a neuro
muscular co-ordination skill.

The experience of many teachers is that 30 minutes is too
short and it seems likely that you can only stick to 30 minute
lessons if you have a tightly organized system with someone
else, like a secretary, to handle all the organization. It's obvious
that if a teacher has to handle money and appointments for
himself, he's unlikely to make a 30 minute timetable workable
Many of us find it puts both the teacher and the student under
pressure for time, whereas 40 minutes gives a little bit of extra

leeway. Once again, newly qualified teachers find they spend more time than that. They give lessons that last 50 to 60 minutes. They feel they can't do anything useful in less time. Now there's nothing wrong with that but it's a good discipline to aim gradually to cut down the time. Of course, as most teachers get more skilful, everything tends to speed up anyway. I remember when I began teaching, that if I put someone onto the table it took a whole 30 minutes just to go round doing the basic procedures. Now that happens in 10 minutes.

Another thing to bear in mind is that the amount of Alexander work appropriate for any individual varies to quite a phenomenal degree. Some years ago, when some of us ran a weekend course in Holland for the first time, we charged quite a lot of money to cover our travel and accommodation costs. We felt a bit guilty about it, so we decided we had to give the participants a tremendous amount of work for their money. I think we gave them 6 hours on Saturday and 6 hours on the Sunday. Because there was a high teacher/student ratio it meant that everyone got a lot of individual work. By Sunday morning, some people either didn't turn up or, when they arrived, just went out into the back garden saying, 'No thanks. I've had enough!' A few other people were already showing signs that the work was reaching a very emotional level – crying, laughing, giggling and exhibiting signs of saturation – yet there were others who wanted more and more and appeared to be a long way from saturation.

I've had that experience since then as well. I can think of a particular example a few years back of a man who came for a lesson three times a week for a month or two but then because he was leaving the country increased the number of lessons in order to get as much experience as possible before he left. He started having a lesson a day and as the time of departure grew nearer he had a lesson with me in the morning and a lesson with another teacher in the afternoon. In the last two weeks before he was due to leave, he booked two lessons every morning with me and two lessons every afternoon with the other teacher. He was having two hours a day of Alexander work and he positively thrived on it. He felt he couldn't conceive of having too much. Yet there are other people for whom even 30 minutes a week is a lot and with whom you find that after 20 to 25 minutes you feel you should coast through the last few minutes because their nervous system has had enough. Incidentally, that same man returned four years later, saying both he and his family were delighted with the effects. He had a few more lessons, which he described as 'recharging his battery.'

**SC: Why is it thought desirable for a new student to come two or three times a week, and then, after a few weeks, to come once a week?**

JN: When Alexander was running his own practice between the wars, he apparently insisted that anyone starting lessons had to come five days a week for three weeks. If they weren't willing to go along with this condition, they didn't start. So what tended to happen was that people outside London would arrange to come up to town for a three week holiday to fit in the schedule. Even in the last 20 years, teachers have preferred new students to come three times a week for the first few weeks.

Nowadays we have to take several things into account. First, social factors. There are fewer people with either the leisure or the money to come every day. Even to come for a lesson three times a week is hard for a lot of people earning an average income. Second, there is the possibility that people learn quicker these days. Something like the Alexander Technique is easier to absorb today than it was 50 years ago. I think it's highly likely that younger people today are more open to this sort of thing. They certainly are more into body awareness.

For example, having someone work on you physically – touching you – is perhaps much easier for people to accept than 50 years ago. Of course, the idea that muscular tension may have something to do with one's mind is almost common sense nowadays. The very term psychosomatic is, after all, part of our everyday language. So perhaps it is not so necessary to insist on our students coming 5 times a week.

Having Alexander lessons is not dissimilar from learning to drive, sing, type or ride a horse. If a person starts by having just one lesson a week it will take much longer to make progress because the input to his neuromuscular system will have lost a lot of its effect 7 days later. The individual is learning how to re-programme himself and, to begin with, that requires short time lapses in order to establish a momentum for the new use and co-ordination. As I say, I think that would be true of any skill requiring neuromuscular co-ordination.

SC: **What can really be achieved with one lesson a week over a long period of time?**

JN: So much depends on the individual. The Technique has been taught for so long that it would be possible to get testimonials which range from, 'I used to get this pain in my right shoulder if I sat at my desk all day and now there's no pain anymore', which is a worthwhile achievement, to: 'Well, it's changed my whole life and outlook'. It can achieve anything from the relief of minor aches and pains to a totally different attitude to life. Look at people like John Dewey and Aldous Huxley and what they wrote about the Technique. They began having a lot of lessons close together in the first few weeks and then had a lesson a week for a while, proceeding to a lesson here and there as and when they could; yet they both wrote about the profound effects the Technique had on their lives.

I think the message is: once you've got started, keep it up over a long time and that may well produce profound effects. For some people the Technique becomes a continuing process of personal discipline. They may have lessons once a week for many years or they may stop for a while and come back occasionally for a refresher course. They'll develop their own pattern of when they want their lessons best to suit themselves. A process is set up within them and all a teacher need say is: 'Right, you tell me when you want lessons, how often, and so on'.

I think a lot of people on training courses underestimate the value of this approach because they receive such intensive work and have, perhaps, forgotten their own path of development. I remember when I was halfway through my training I couldn't imagine what could be achieved with one lesson a week. It seemed so little compared to what I was getting on a training course. I had to remind myself to look back at how I'd felt before I came on the training course when I was having a lesson a week for a year or so. At that time I felt it was the most important thing that had ever happened to me and it was a major influence on my life. The real test in all this is seeing people who've had private lessons over years and years. It's then you realise it can make a big difference to people's lives.

**SC: Okay, I accept that. But then what use is, say, a batch of 20 or 25 lessons?**

JN: Most people are careful when it comes to spending money. They won't have more than a handful of Alexander lessons if they think it's a waste of time. A lot of people may well become permanently free of all sorts of niggling complaints in a course of 20 or 25 lessons. They may also acquire a lot of body awareness so an alarm system is set up which tells them when they are using themselves badly. Something inside them says: 'Hey! This is uncomfortable. I don't like this. This is doing me harm.' That sense may well remain with them for life and that's a tremendous achievement. For example, there was a chiropractor who had scarcely more than 20 lessons from me. A year later he came back for a refresher and said: 'The improvement in my general level of health and well-being has been absolutely remarkable and longlasting.' I also like to quote the Norwegian opera singer who had 20–25 lessons on the advice of her singing teacher. Her command of English was charmingly eccentric and she said to me: 'Before I come to have Alexander lessons I feel very well, but now, after lessons, I feel weller than well!'.

# CHAPTER 7

# Teaching the Tools of Self-Help

**SC: How much information do you give to a student at any one time?**

JN: I think there's an overwhelming temptation for new teachers to tell students everything they know in the first lesson. But bombarding people with information is often counter-productive; there's no way the Alexander Technique can be taught in one lesson. A mass of information will only bewilder people and anyway they won't remember what you're saying.

I suppose one common sense rule about teaching is that in any one lesson just one new fact is normally enough. For example, if a teacher explains about head balance, that will be sufficient information for that one lesson. Similarly, to explain the idea of back lengthening should be enough for one lesson. I say this not simply from an Alexander point of view, but from a psychology of learning perspective. One new fact in a 30 or 40 minute lesson is about as much as most people can absorb!

So the teacher has to feed information to people slowly. You have to do it several times and in various ways. You can't assume that because you've explained something to somebody once they'll grasp it right away. Just as one's own understanding as a teacher of the Alexander Technique grows and evolves into a deepening insight, so you want your student's understanding to grow and evolve. Sometimes you'll find a student will say: 'I've never realised that before' after you've explained something, even though you may have said it many times previously! When that happens it's often because the student has just had the experience which connects to what you're saying. This is another good reason why the teacher shouldn't let the information he provides outrun the student's practical experience. Apart from anything else, people can get frustrated. It's revealing that many find a theoretical understanding of how the Technique works makes it harder for them to put it into practice.

Indeed, one of the things that makes a teacher's heart sink slightly is to have someone come in for their first lesson and tell you they've read every book that's ever been written about the Alexander Technique. Ideally the theory should go hand in hand with practice. So you can see why patience is essential for both the teacher and the student. It's part of the teacher's job to get the student to realise that patience is necessary – that the process does take time and that amassing a vast amount of theoretical knowledge is not going to help anyone learn any faster.

**SC: When would you introduce a student to lying down work?**

JN: It's another one of those things you can't make absolute rules about. There will always be students who will be exceptions, perhaps with unusual difficulties. However, most people can be introduced to lying down work as early as possible – right from the first lesson. It's a very beneficial practice. You see most people are in an over-stimulated, over-reactive, wound up state. Anything that makes them stop and devote time to themselves to undo, unravel and unwind is bound to be beneficial. That's why, for most people leading harassed lives in modern conditions, virtually any form of relaxation is better than nothing.

Lying on the floor semi-supine, as we recommend, has several advantages. The physical position itself encourages important changes in the body. If someone lies in semi-supine with the head supported, the neck unsupported and the knees bent pointing upwards, it means that gravity is encouraging the whole of the back to spread out, the spine to lengthen and the neck to drop back slightly in relation to the head. These are, of course, aspects of 'undoing'. Lying down is a tremendously important discipline for students and teachers: it's a means whereby you can give yourself an Alexander lesson.

A further aspect of lying down is that in semi-supine the floor gives a lot of helpful feedback to the nervous system. Most people have very little 'back consciousness': they are very aware of the front of their bodies; it is the area they see when they look in the mirror and they can feel a lot of what is happening in their front. They rarely know, to any significant degree, the shape of their back and spine, and have very little feeling or conception of the musculature of the back. People often are not aware of the unnecessary tensions in their back, until those tensions reach the point where they are doing damage and producing pain. Regularly putting one's back on a firm, flat surface allows a person to become conscious of the back and its relationship to the neck and head.

**SC: Why do you think people are unaware of their back?**

JN: My guess is that most of us are so chronically shortened in the back muscles that we simply cease to register it. It is the same in any other part of the body. When muscles are chronically shortened for some time, the brain starts to interpret that shortening as 'normal' and no longer registers it as tension and contraction until or unless it produces pain. One might also speculate that there is a very strong tendency for people to identify psychologically with their front: after all their front is what they present to the world and what they usually see when they look in a mirror.

**SC: Have you ever had a student fall asleep on the table? Not through boredom, of course. I wouldn't want to imply that!**

JN: I had a student who used to snore loudly after a few minutes on the table.

**SC: So what do you do? Is it of any use to carry on working?**

JN: No, I don't think so. All that part of the neuromuscular system concerned with upright balance and support just switches off when you go to sleep. Plus the fact that there's no scope for conscious learning. I think you have to wake the person up and explain that it's a waste of their money to sleep through a lesson. It may then be best for them to get off the table as they're less likely to feel dozy when upright. You might also look at the room temperature and so on. Is it a bit too warm and stuffy?

If it happens repeatedly with a particular student, you may need to ask if he can get some more sleep or come at a different time of day.

**SC: When and how do you introduce 'the directions'.**

JN: Teachers vary greatly in how they approach this. You can, for example, introduce the idea of directing during lying down. When the student is on the table, you can go on to explain that the semi-supine position encourages the body to lengthen. Now that means, in particular, that the spine must be lengthening, since the spine with its series of curves and separate vertebrae interspersed with cushioning discs is the part of the body most susceptible to excessive compression and distortion.

If the spine is going to lengthen, then it is crucial that the neck muscles which connect the base of the skull to the upper body are releasing to let the head come away from the shoulders. It is no good wishing to lengthen if your neck muscles are pulling your head into your shoulders. That's like trying to drive your car with the handbrake on. Also, the back muscles don't all run in vertical strips up and down the spine. Some of them fan outwards from the spine, so the back has to spread widthways as well as lengthways, particularly to allow free breathing. That's a quick and easy way to explain why 'neck free, head out, back to lengthen and widen' is a necessary set of directions.

Perhaps I should add here that I've also found the subject of directing emerges spontaneously to some extent and, therefore, where you start may depend on what the other person says and what their particular problems are. I've often found it useful to explain to people that in all activities of life, including the very basic activity of supporting themselves against gravity, they tend to produce a lot of muscle tension and effort, thus shortening the whole body. If someone is clenching and tightening the muscles in any part of the neck, trunk and limbs, they are inevitably, as Alexander pointed out, reducing their total stature. It is a simple fact about the body that muscle contraction produces shortening of stature: there is a decrease in distance between the head and heels. The teacher's task is to help people overcome the tendency to approach every situation by contracting themselves and teach them how to approach every situation by expanding themselves. One might say the Alexander Technique is about 'expansion in activity' rather than 'contraction in activity.' So the directions relating to the head, neck, back and limbs are the detailed working out of that primary direction which is towards expansion.

Directing is having the wish, the intention, the aspiration, to be going in those directions that are expansive rather than contractive, but the wish must be expressed through muscular release rather than tension and effort. We should also be careful to emphasize to students to release and direct in a particular order – neck, head, back, and limbs. The process works like a combination lock. There are certain keys that must be turned in a certain order if the whole mechanism is going to unlock and expand. It's as simple as that.

Another important element in teaching a student is that the

idea of directions is almost inevitably introduced using words which, at first, will have very little content or meaning. The long-term process of Alexander lessons is for the teacher to use his hands in such a way as to give the student an experience at the neuromuscular level which then gives content to those empty symbols. It is, of course, a long-term process, and so our real skill as teachers is to give concrete reality to verbal description and analysis.

Some people have described this as a conditioning process. They claim that by constantly repeating the experience and associating it with the verbal labels the teacher is setting up a conditioned reflex. But conditioning can be a mindless exercise, so I think it would be both more accurate and more desirable to see it as the student gaining from the lessons an ever deepening understanding of what is happening. The basic directions gain greater and greater kinaesthetic content so that, ultimately, the student becomes his own teacher and can take charge of what he is doing to himself.

A very common experience amongst students when they begin having Alexander lessons is that they feel better after a lesson but the feeling lasts for only a short period of time. Then, after a few more lessons, it lasts a bit longer and after a while you often hear people say, 'I feel much better, but I don't have control over that feeling. It gradually fades out until the next lesson.' If the teacher encourages students to make a practice of lying down, when they get up again they will find they recapture some of the benefits they get from their Alexander lessons. Gradually, as students go further, they find that just stopping and directing for themselves at any time brings back some of the benefits of their lessons too. Once that happens students are increasingly becoming their own teachers.

Now of course, good Alexander teachers will for a long time be able to take students further than they can go by themselves, because there are so many things to unravel. On the physiological level, the reason for this is that the body consists of several layers of muscle between the skin and the bones. Then there are fascial sheets that wrap around each layer of muscle and further layers of connective tissue over the organs. So, with all these layers that interweave with each other there is always the possibility of things becoming snarled, contracted, distorted and fixed. On top of all that, the stresses of life are continually restimulating our habitual patterns of contraction and tension, although over time the Alexander student will be more and more able to inhibit these patterns. This means there is scope for improvement to go on for a very long time. Sometimes people at first find that very depressing but it need not be at all. Apart from anything else, it means the Technique never becomes boring and things will always get better. That's a rather remarkable prospect.

**SC: Some teachers encourage students to use visualisation techniques in order to bring about 'undoing'. You mentioned earlier the idea of imagining one's head to be a helium-filled balloon. Others have misgivings about this approach. What's your view?**

JN: There's one thing a teacher can rely on – if it works it's okay. And you should be able to feel if it works through your hands on the student. You see it always has to be borne in mind that people's mental processes work in different ways. The very word 'think' seems to mean different things to different people. If you say, 'think of your neck releasing and your head going forward and up,' some people find it necessary to translate that into a visual image. For example, if you can feel someone releasing and going up and you ask them what they are thinking of and they reply: 'I'm imagining my head as a balloon floating up on the end of a piece of string and a pair of lead-filled boots taking my feet into the ground at the other end,' that's fine. I've even heard the story of a man who, if he did what he thought was stiffening his neck, he released it, which allowed his head to go forward and up. He'd got into such a disturbed and distorted state in terms of sensory appreciation, that what he thought was stiffening his neck was really an undoing!

But overall I think it's very useful for students to have a simple understanding of the anatomical structure so that their directing stays close to anatomical reality. Then there's less likelihood of the student drifting off into the realms of pure fantasy. You see, what we as teachers don't want, is the student who can quite happily close his eyes and see in his 'mind's eye' wonderfully precise pictures of his head floating up to the sky and his whole body expanding, and yet none of that information is being transmitted from the brain to the body. It stays at the level of a 'head trip'. Directing is not like that at all. It's worth quoting Alexander here:

'When I employ the words 'direction' and 'directed' with

'use' in such phrases as 'direction of my use' and 'I directed the use,' etc, I wish to indicate the process involved in projecting messages from the brain to the mechanisms and in conducting the energy necessary to the use of these mechanisms.'[1]

It's clear from this quote that directing is the conducting of messages and energy from the brain to parts of the body and that seeing pictures in one's head runs the risk of simply using the visual mechanism of the brain and not the sensory-motor connections to the whole body. As someone's experience of the Technique grows and develops, it's as if their mind and body become more and more integrated, so that consciousness permeates the whole body instead of simply staying in the head, or, as we were saying earlier, in the front of the body. In this process you begin to become much more aware of the whole body so that it's possible to experience and appreciate tensions and distortions. You begin, for instance, to appreciate the shape of your own neck and how your head balances on top of it. As that experience deepens, so too does the ability to reduce tensions and distortions. It is as if perception and direction get closer to each other. That ties in with the experience of teachers like Krishnamurti who say observation and awareness by themselves bring about change.

---

'We have seen that we live in a gravitational field: it is essential for us therefore to go up against gravity. But of course gravity is operating all the time, so because this is a constant factor in all our lives, we need the constant reminder to go up. So when you look at the directions or orders they are not just something that you remember from time to time, that you give at the critical moment, or are applicable now and then. The four orders are applicable all the time; you give them all the time.

'You don't pronounce them all the time; you don't necessarily put them into words all the time. It is because you understand this and the concept, that they are part of your attitude to life, what you want in life. And when you get it to that stage, you have got it made, and until you get it to that stage, you haven't.'

From an unpublished transcript of a talk by Walter Carrington to his training course on the 24th July 1972.

---

**SC: At what point in a series of lessons would you introduce the concept of inhibition?**

[1] *The Use of the Self* by F.M. Alexander, p. 20n (1946 edition).

JN: It's all part of a teacher's skill to know when to introduce inhibition. I've had examples of students with whom one wouldn't want to introduce much in the way of talking about inhibition for a very long time. I've also seen examples of students whose teachers from the very beginning have tried to make them 'inhibit' in a very stereotyped way and it's nearly put them off the Alexander Technique because it created so much extra disturbance.

For people to apply inhibition consciously requires a quietness and integration in the nervous system. People who are overstimulated are scarcely capable of applying any sort of inhibition, and asking them to do so very often results in an increase in tension (stress) rather than a decrease. They're already at war with themselves. To ask them to inhibit under those conditions will get them to use so-called 'willpower' as a means to whip everything into line and create even more internal warfare and confusion. Very often the first step in getting across to a student the idea of inhibition is to help them come to a state of quietness.

I have heard Miss Margaret Goldie quote F. M. Alexander as saying: 'Choose to be quiet throughout your whole body, with particular attention to the neck and head.'

This is one of the most important aspects of teaching the Technique as I mentioned earlier. It's the transmission through the teacher's hands of a level of centredness and stillness to the student that makes inhibition a possibility for them. It will then be quite easy and quite natural for them, rather than something that creates conflict and tension.

With these considerations in mind, the teacher will have to assess by observation and experience when to introduce the concept of inhibition to each new student. There can be no fixed rules about such things.

**SC: So how do you go about teaching inhibition?**

JN: This is a complex subject, so any discussion of it is necessarily going to be rather intricate.

Let's be clear first of all that inhibition doesn't mean being shy, awkward, or repressed. We use the word in its neurological sense, where it refers to the way reactions programmed in to some parts of the nervous system can be kept in check by inhibitory messages from other parts of the nervous system. It's just like a traffic signal with green light for GO and red light for STOP. The inhibitory messages are the red light.

A widespread way of teaching inhibition is where teachers drill the student by saying: 'Now I want you to go into the chair. Stop and say "No," give your directions, and then proceed.' I've never been very happy with this approach. It's always seemed to me to be unrealistic because inhibition is the reverse side of direction. If one thinks of a human being as an energy system, then what an Alexander teacher is trying to do is to allow the student to send his energy along the right channels rather than the wrong ones. It's obvious then that energy has to be both directed down the right channels and also stopped from going down the wrong ones. It's the stopping of the energy going down the wrong pathways that's the inhibitory side and sending it down the right pathways that's the direction side.

More and more I see inhibition and direction as very closely related. You can't have one without the other. That's probably the reason both Alexander and Frank Pierce Jones seem to write about inhibition as if it included direction. If one is inhibiting any interference with the primary control, then the direction side of things is implied by the fact that if someone inhibits all the wrong things, the right thing will do itself.

One of the obvious difficulties in that way of teaching inhibition as: 'Stop, say "No", give your directions and then proceed' is that it isn't carrying inhibition all the way through the action. It's necessary not only to inhibit the energy going down the wrong channels at the start of an activity, but also all the way through an action. Just as direction and awareness have to be 'thinking in activity,' so too does inhibition have to be 'thinking in activity.' Inhibition can't be seen as something that is just done at the beginning of an activity, followed later by something called directing! Inhibition and direction are both part of 'thinking in activity.'

It helps enormously to know this process already happens in people. Just as the primary control already functions in human beings and animals (albeit badly in most humans) and isn't something F.M. Alexander has invented, so it's the same with inhibition. It's built in to the nervous system. Messages from one part of the nervous system to another can be either excitatory (the green light) or inhibitory (the red light). Junctions in the nervous system have to assess the balance of excitatory and inhibitory messages they are receiving and act accordingly.

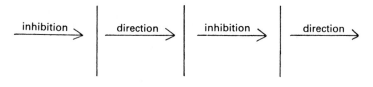

*Figure 5*

We simply want to encourage people to use inhibition and primary control better and more consciously. But inhibition functions to some extent in everyone. Somebody once told me the only situation where the inhibitory mechanism doesn't work at all is when a person is suffering from strychnine poisoning. This apparently breaks down all the inhibitory mechanisms of the nervous system and there is a complete spasm of the musculature.

So for most people, inhibition is operating but it's operating largely unconsciously. All those people skilled in the performance of complex activities, musicians, athletes and so on, know perfectly well about using inhibition in activity. They know from learning their skill that there are a series of things they must do and a series of things they must not do, because those are the things that will interfere with their performance. Good tennis players, for instance, know they must not bend the wrist, let the racket head drop or get their feet too near the bounce of the ball. They know, too, that they must stay at the back of the court until the right moment arrives when it's an advantage to come to the net. These are all forms of inhibition.

In the Alexander Technique we are simply asking people to become more conscious of the inhibitory process and to apply with a special kind of precision to the balance of the body. But

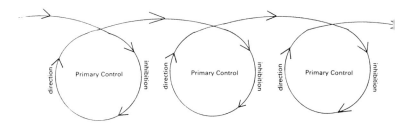

*Figure 6*

to say to a top-level tennis player, 'Stop, say No, give your directions and then proceed to play your stroke,' would mean that he will tumble down the international ranks very quickly! It can't be applied that way.

Primary control is of course also part of the interrelationship between inhibition and direction. What are we inhibiting and directing for if not to facilitate that co-ordination of head, neck and trunk F. M. Alexander termed the primary control? Also implied is release of excessive tension, since it is by release that the primary control is facilitated. So we might illustrate this graphically. Figure 5 shows a view of inhibition and direction as a linear sequence. Figure 6 shows a more complex view of inhibition, direction and primary control in a circular relationship.

We need to inhibit in order to direct to facilitate the primary control, so that as our use improves we become better able to inhibit in order to direct to facilitate the primary control to improve our use, so that we become better able to inhibit . . . and so on. Individual lessons can help impart a momentum to this circular process, until, like a flywheel, the circle develops a momentum of its own in the student's daily life.

Now, to take this a step further, the inhibitory side, stopping the energy going down the wrong channels, does have to come first. Although I've said inhibition is the reverse side of direction, to be faithful to the complexity of the subject we should express it as an arrow with the two sides out of synch. Figure 7 is therefore a close-up of one of the circles from Figure 6, showing inhibition and direction as two sides of the same arrow, but with inhibition always slightly ahead.

Some attempt to inhibit the habitual responses that contract and unbalance us must precede the conscious direction of an

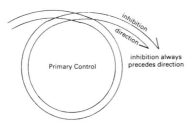

*Figure 7*

improved use, but the inhibition must continue throughout the direction, otherwise we are fighting against ourselves.

So at some point the teacher needs to introduce the idea to the student that it is possible to consciously inhibit one's reactions to a stimulus, whether the stimulus is an external situation or an internal thought or feeling. It is possible simply to refrain from reacting in order to take time to decide how to react, or not to react at all. The interrelationship of inhibition and direction becomes apparent again here, because we are first of all attempting to inhibit those muscular tension reactions which will disturb the primary control, the balance of the body's central core, the head, neck and back. Continuing to inhibit those tension reactions involves projecting directions to release the neck, allow the head to go forward and up, and the back to lengthen and widen, while considering how to respond to the situation.

In the early stages of Alexander learning this will be a matter of learning how to respond to a stimulus to move by inhibiting contracted movement habits and finding a way to make simple everyday movements without clenching the neck and back muscles. Later, this can be extended to the inhibition of unwanted habitual behavioural responses so that we can respond more constructively.

**SC: All this talk of inhibition sounds very self-conscious and analytical. Isn't it likely to kill all spontaneity?**

JN: Quite the opposite! Inhibition in our sense is precisely what allows something new to emerge. If spontaneity is taken to mean always acting on your first impulse, your behaviour may well be socially outrageous, but it would soon become outrageous in very predictable ways. Withholding response allows time to reflect and consider one's options.

Let me read you a passage about this, beautifully expressed, written by a trainee-teacher in the second year of her three year training:

'If I inhibit a habitual response to a stimulus right throughout an activity, I give myself space to respond in a different way. I don't actually know what this way will be in any given moment, so I rely on natural creative processes at work within myself. My initial habitual responses do not disappear just because I might allow new experiences to occur once, or even many times. Over time, what does seem to happen, is a 'building-up' of my own natural forces, which I can contribute to, by remembering to inhibit my habitual responses. Then, when the time is right, something falls into place, and some part of my habitual response seems to disappear. I find this absolutely fantastic, but true, as far as I can tell. When this moment of realisation arrives, I feel so 'right' and completely at peace with myself. This feeling is always highlighted, because as the 'build-up' occurs, I experience ever increasing conflict between my habits and new experiences. I dread this battle, but it seems to be necessary and important to work through, in order for me to accept and integrate the new experiences.

'This whole cycle happens at all levels – psychological included. I can, and often do, interfere with the process, by not allowing it to continue or by over-analysing what is going on at a particular time. Alternatively, I can give consent to the ongoing process, by inhibiting my habitual responses, including my response of over-analysis. I am therefore not deliberately considering every move I make, or every thought I have.

'I have found this kind of inhibition very helpful in dealing with one of my greatest problems in life: unnecessary fear. In the past, my only way of coping with fear, was to suppress it. This was actively encouraged, and indeed, expected, by those around me. I found suppression of this unwanted fear, a sickening experience, which in the long run only made things worse. Now, when things 'come together' for me, I don't feel scared at all, but even quietly confident! It feels truly wonderful. As well, my habitual response is nowhere near as extreme as it used to be. I am delighted that at last I am really dealing with fear.

'So I regard Alexander's Technique as brilliant. By inhibiting a habitual response, the space allowed enables me to experience something new, which is slowly developed, until I am strong enough not to need all of my old habits. The unnecessary parts go away. It's as simple as that.'[2]

From Amanda Dunningham, Melbourne Alexander Teacher Training School, 1988.

# CHAPTER 8

# The Teacher–Student Relationship

**SC: If, in a lesson, a student becomes disturbed for any reason, how should the teacher respond?**

JN: Well, there may often be a lot of casual conversation in a lesson and if subjects come up which a student gets very heated about, it might be better to steer clear of those areas. For example, some time ago a woman came to me for a lesson in a very agitated state about the day's political news. There had been an event she felt very strongly about and as soon as she arrived she started sounding off to me. She was getting so worked up that the intensity of her emotion was magnifying all those muscular patterns which we were trying to do something about.

I thought it necessary to say: 'Look, you're here for an Alexander lesson and you're paying me for this time. If you spend the whole lesson talking about this subject, you're not going to get much from the lesson. It will be almost impossible for me to do anything useful.' To which she replied, 'I don't care. I feel so strongly about this, I've got to talk about it!' She then proceeded to do just that while I put my hands on her in an attempt to ensure that things didn't get any worse. At the end she happily wrote out a cheque for me, and said, 'Yes, I feel much better for having got that out of my system!' I felt quite satisfied with the outcome because I'd given her a choice and, at the time, she felt it was worthwhile paying money to spend the lesson talking about the issue rather than not talking about it.

It's interesting at a general level here, that the subjects which generate the most heated discussions are people's religious and political convictions. They tend to hold these so strongly that the degree and intensity of the convictions winds a student up so much and so quickly it makes the teacher's task a very difficult one. The moral of the story is for the teacher not to get into arguments about very emotive subjects, not least because it's of very little benefit to the student. It would be about as sensible as going along to a meditation class seeking peace and tranquillity and then spending the time preparing a diatribe on law and order for the next Conservative Association meeting.

SC: **I've heard several teachers complain they're at a loss to know what to do when a student has an emotional release in a lesson and starts crying or laughing uncontrollably. What do you do?**

N: This is indeed something we are not trained to deal with and perhaps we should be. I think it is fair to say it is one of those things that's more likely to happen now rather than 50 years ago simply because people are more open about their feelings and willing to express them these days.

Of course, it is as well to recognise that releasing contractions and fixations at a muscular level affects the psyche; but an emotional outburst such as breaking down in floods of tears or coming out with a fit of anger doesn't happen as often as one might imagine in Alexander lessons, particularly, if one reads accounts of other 'physical' ways of working, such as neo-Reichian therapy, bioenergetics and some types of massage. That it doesn't often happen in Alexander lessons is sometimes used as a criticism of the Alexander Technique by practitioners in other psycho-physical disciplines and therapies. They claim Alexander Technique teachers only work on the body and don't let anything happen emotionally. Because people so rarely cry in an Alexander lesson, they claim that nothing much can be happening at an emotional level. Now it's true some Alexander teachers are frightened by these things – they don't want to talk about them and they don't want them to happen – but it's also true that in the nature of the way we work and the way in which we use our hands, we are transmitting a stimulus of a kind that both calms and integrates the nervous system.

So whilst there might be a good deal of loosening of the 'muscular armouring,' to use the Reichian terminology, it may often be accompanied, not so much by the explosion of locked feelings, as by a profound sense of relief and calm.

I've also sometimes found that although there might not be much of an emotional outburst in the lesson itself, it might happen between lessons. I've had students say: 'Do you know, after last week's lesson I went home and cried and felt very sad but then the next day I felt very much better.' Or: 'After the lesson last week I went into a shop and I lost my temper. I was

so furious, I got so angry. I can't understand why.' Or again
'I've been terribly depressed since the last lesson and I've been
remembering things from my past which I'd totally forgotten
about.' These sorts of things do sometimes come up between
lessons but not usually in a disturbing fashion. Once again,
think it's because our work is to do with the integration of the
system as well as an opening of the blocks.

I would say that, in general, it's easier to handle those emotions in another person that we can handle in ourselves. It
follows then that we will be frightened by the appearance of
those emotions in another person, that are frightening when
they appear in ourselves. Therefore one of the best ways of
coping with the emotions of our students is to learn to cope
with our own emotions. And for some of us, that may mean
finding appropriate help in our own psychological self-explo-
ration. Then we will be able to accept what is happening in our
students without feeling threatened by it.

However, if we start presenting ourselves as quasi-psycho-
therapists, we are inviting a big load of psychological transference and projection.

SC: **How do you see the phenomenon of transference between a
student and an Alexander teacher? Dr. Barlow, for example
claims that, 'there is often an initial 'honeymoon' period of
great pleasure in having discovered not only something which
explains previous troubles but which also offers solutions,
and that 'some people continue their happy honeymoon into a
long and successful marriage'.[1] What ought to be the nature of
the relationship between teacher and student?**

JN: I think teacher and student should have a cooperative relationship based on the premise that they are equal people. In many
ways, it's a professional relationship. When any of us goes to
see a professional, we go on the basis that we are paying for
their services and that the professional happens to have a
specific skill we don't have. It's not a question of superiority
and inferiority. Quite simply, the Alexander teacher has a skill
the student doesn't and so we are being paid to pass on that
skill with the conscious intention of helping the pupil to take
responsibility for his actions.

Now transference is a problem in this and although it isn't
often talked about, it perhaps needs to be. Alexander teachers

[1] *The Alexander Principle* by Dr. W. Barlow pp. 171–172 (Gollancz 1973).

should be aware of transference, and that holds for any quasi-therapeutic, one-to-one situation where people are talking about the problems they might have and the teacher is in some way helping them. So although we don't call ourselves therapists because we are more in the area of human potential, we would nonetheless to outsiders come within the broad category known as 'the helping professions.' In other words, many people would tend to view the Alexander teacher in terms of the 'therapist' model, and transference often does take place because of this. Some students will see the teacher as a parent figure. Alternatively, if the teacher is around the appropriate age and within the category of the student's sexual preference the student can project a whole series of images onto the teacher from previous or imagined experience of sexual relationships.

**SC: In certain forms of psychotherapy transference is used as part of the treatment, isn't it?**

JN: Yes. In that kind of work, the task of the therapist is to encourage the client to become increasingly conscious of what it is he's projecting as a way for the client to scrutinise the inner dynamics of the psyche. This is a highly skilled job and a dangerous business to meddle with if you don't know what you're dealing with because transference can be a very explosive process. I might also mention in this context the opposite phenomenon of counter-transference which is the process whereby the therapist projects certain things onto the client. That's something the Alexander teacher must watch for too. If a teacher repeatedly falls in love with his students, it might be relevant to ask himself what is the nature of that particular projection. Or if the teacher finds himself continually irritated by certain types of student and experiences an irrational resentment of them, then it would again be wise for him to consider the process through which those feelings are generated. That is part of one's responsibility as a professional.

To return to the initial question of projection from the student onto the Alexander teacher, it is not part of our job nor is it in our training to deal with people therapeutically. I think the best way of handling these situations is by defusing them and constantly creating an environment which makes them unlikely to happen. Most professionals learn to do this through experience. Consider the 'bedside manner' of the doctor. It's a soothing and patient, but also impersonal, business-like manner. The whole idea of the doctor's white coat is an important and visible component in the social construction of impersonality. Now Alexander teachers don't wear white coats, but nevertheless we can learn how through tone of voice, phrasing and general manner to convey a degree of warmth and friendliness combined with a degree of detachment. This does not mean coldness but rather a sort of impersonal benevolence of the very best kind.

A lot of what I'm talking about is common sense. It's all about having a reasonable and realistic assessment of oneself as a teacher. A sense of irony and a sense of humour are very useful in this respect. So too, is a recognition that one does not know everything. One way of defusing many situations of transference is for the teacher to resist any urge to set himself up as 'god-like'. There's no point in a teacher pretending he has the answer to every question a student comes up with, which would, in any case, tend to feed the parent image. An Alexander teacher is not in any sense a guru.

I might add here that there are always some people with whom one will fail. At times it might be necessary to send them to another teacher or to another form of help. Fortunately, this doesn't happen very often, but it is sometimes necessary to tell people that you are not a psychiatrist, nor are you their mother or father, nor even a priest, and if this is what they want they'd better go to the relevant agency. If that is not made clear, the teacher may find himself being fed into a psychic mincer by some very manipulative and disturbed people. The teacher must have a sense of his own personal limits and an awareness of the limits of his professional skills which will allow him to say, 'No, I'm not going to deal with this. I don't have to and I don't choose to. Will you please go somewhere else.' Establishing boundaries is vital in any teaching or therapeutic role.

SC: **Following on from this last point, I remember one senior Alexander teacher telling me that the Technique should never become an 'instrument of sadism', by which I took him to mean a method of domination and a means of obtaining power over another individual.**

JN: Yes, it's interesting in this respect that newly qualified teachers often suffer from a terrible feeling of inferiority and a complete lack of confidence, which means they are very tentative at first in approaching their students. It is of course, necessary for teachers to develop a sense of confidence in their skills and most teachers do eventually. Having got over the initial lack of confidence, it is easy then to slip over to the other extreme and say: 'Gosh! I have this wonderful gift of the Alexander Technique. All these people come and see me. I put my hands on them and I feel how tense, tight, fixed and pulled down they are, whereas I'm so up, open and free at all levels. What a wonderful person I am and what a mess the rest of humanity is!'

There is, then, a real danger of teachers developing a rather superior, even patronising, manner with their students. This is very dangerous of course, and something to be avoided. If it isn't, then those students who come for lessons will take on a dependent role and, in the long term, the teacher is harming himself in becoming fixed in that superior and condescending attitude.

So I think having consciously worked to root out the initial feelings of insecurity and anxiety the teacher should also go on to root out all these feelings of superiority and any desire to impress his students. All those feelings and attitudes, you see, are a barrier to a genuinely cooperative teacher-student relationship. It should be remembered that the students are there for their own benefit, not for the oiling of the teacher's ego.

**SC:** **Some students complain they have 'good' and 'bad' days and they would much prefer to be at their most favourable level all the time. What would you say to them?**

JN: I don't think learning the Alexander Technique is very different to learning any other skill in this respect. Take music students – they have good and bad days, don't they? So, too, do typists, tennis players, mathematicians, plumbers, even those with a great deal of experience.

I'm inclined to think that when we have the desire to be on a high level all the time we suffer from the illusory search for perfection we talked about earlier. It's all part of the myth that 'one day I will attain such perfect use in myself that I will coast along effortlessly without ever deviating from it.' Life's not like that.

Nothing in this world maintains itself in such a state of static perfection. Everyone is going to wake up some mornings not feeling as good as the day before. Fortunately there are also days that you wake up feeling terrific and everything goes well.

**SC: Does the same thing apply to teachers?**

JN: Yes, of course, a teacher may be working better some days than others. It's all relative. Provided that you as the teacher carry on working according to the principles you've been taught, looking after yourself as much as possible, you'll always be benefiting your students, even if some days you don't feel as good as on other days. You don't rely on 'feeling good'; you just carry on applying the principles.

It's worth putting the problem in perspective. Five years from now both teacher and student will be having 'good' and 'bad' days, but a 'bad' day in five years time may well be better than a 'good' day now. In other words, as with the acquisition of most complex skills, one is on an ascending spiral so that one's current low points are higher than the high spots of a few years previously.

**SC: Do you think a teacher can assume his use will be better than his student's?**

JN: No. You see in a simple way of analysing it, some students may be in a better state and a better condition than their teacher; and yet the teacher may well be of considerable benefit to the student. It all hinges on the degree to which use is conscious. It is possible to find athletes who seem to have superb balance and co-ordination but their phenomenal good use operates at an unconscious level. Of course, it's a marvellous attribute, but it's not what Alexander got so excited about. He explored not just 'good use' but 'conscious good use' – having conscious control over the means whereby one attained good use. So the teacher can at least expect to have a more conscious good use than a student, which is always an advantage.

**SC: So the teacher's conscious direction in combination with the student's good use will always produce an improvement?**

JN: Yes. It's bound to produce a positive outcome. The teacher's consciousness brings an extra energy into the process. An analogy is the role of coaches in sports. A coach can be of great benefit to an athlete even when the coach is not so skilled in the particular event. What the coach contributes to the athlete is the objective assessment, analysis and observation.

**SC: On this issue of conscious good use, students often ask: Will I always have to think about this Alexander stuff, or will it eventually become automatic?**

N: In my experience, the answer to that is: Yes, you will always have to think about it, but thinking about it will become automatic. You will eventually find yourself automatically checking whether you have tightened your neck, narrowed your back and so on. It may seem as if it will take a long time to get to that point, but anyone who can drive a car may perhaps remember their first driving lessons. There probably seemed to be so many things to attend to that you could not imagine how all those other people seemed to have mastered it. Yet here you are now, negotiating city traffic, catching the weather forecast on the radio and talking to your passenger, all at the same time!

It may seem contradictory to talk of conscious good use, conscious inhibition and direction becoming automatic. But F.M. actually deals with this point in a long section in *Man's Supreme Inheritance*. After describing the need to change 'incorrect habits of mind and body' into 'correct and beneficial habits', he goes on to say:

> 'I believe I have at last laid myself quite open to the attack of the habitual objector, a person I am really anxious to conciliate. I have given him the opportunity of pointing a finger at my last paragraph and saying, "But you only want to change one habit for another! If, as you have implied, the habit of mind is bad, why encourage habits at all, even if they are as you say, correct and beneficial?"' [2].

The gist of F.M.'s response to this objection is that while conscious guidance and control may become a habit, it is a habit that has been chosen by intelligent decision, and as such it can easily be altered should circumstances require. Incidentally, this certainly doesn't mean that this wonderful new habit of conscious good use is infallible and doesn't require any further work. It just means that the work gets a bit easier and develops a momentum of its own.

C: **Do you conduct a verbal dialogue with students, asking what they're thinking, feeling or observing?**

N: No, not really. Obviously I don't refuse to listen to what students say, and I might at times draw a student's attention to something that's happening. But I don't use questioning as a teaching method. Nor, by all accounts did F.M. It wouldn't fit

*Man's Supreme Inheritance* by F.M. Alexander, pp. 52–55 (1957 edition).

in with his concern about faulty sensory appreciation. You can't re-educate the kinaesthetic sense by words alone.

The tradition of Socratic dialogue, which goes back to Plato assumes that the student already knows the answer subconsciously and merely needs to be led to bringing it into consciousness. One might say that's a very good model for the Alexander Technique, since we're saying that we evoke a natural process in the human body which has been interfered with and is no longer accessible consciously. However, it seems to me that in good Alexander teaching a great deal of the dialogue is kinaesthetic, conducted through the teacher's hands. So often a teacher will be working away and be explaining some aspect of the Technique, and will suddenly say 'There. That's it.' The teacher has felt something change in the student which may give him a better chance of experiencing directly what the teacher is trying to explain verbally.

I've witnessed the verbal dialogue kind of teaching in action and I'm not impressed. Such approaches often seem to me to imply that F.M. himself was too lazy, too stupid or too stubborn to teach that way. I don't buy that.

**SC: How does the Alexander teacher encourage a student to change habits of drinking or drug taking without either being or appearing to be, moralistic and censorious?**

JN: Mostly by reminding students that if they're regularly doing things which are strongly counteracting the effects of the Alexander Technique, like heavy indulgence in drink or drugs, it's a waste of their time and money. The teacher must be objective about this and not morally disapproving as a function of some personal prejudice. Of course, that may often be difficult, but it's something to aim for. I remember one Alexander teacher who said to me in all seriousness that listening to any kind of jazz was 'very pulling down and very bad for people.' Needless to say, he strongly disliked jazz! Now one suspects this was more of a personal prejudice than a serious observation that everyone would inevitably and inexorably pull down if they listened to jazz. Still if you get people turning up for lessons drunk, you'll probably have to say something to them.

**SC: Would you still work on them in that state?**

N: Well, it depends how drunk they were. I did once refuse to work on somebody who came straight from an office party and was so drunk there was no point in him having a lesson. Fortunately, he recognised the fact and went home to sleep it off. I also had someone who came for lessons regularly after long business lunches where he drank a lot of wine and it was a bit like working with someone stuffed with cotton wool. By pointing out that it was a very poor investment drinking three quarters of a bottle of wine before coming for a lesson, it was easy for me to persuade him not to do that.

Most of us know, from personal experience, that our reaction time slows down under the influence of alcohol. However, a lot of people feel very relaxed in that state. Now the irony of it is that very often they're not at all relaxed. There may be a great deal of muscular tension but their brain is simply not registering it. Alcohol acts as a depressant on the nervous system – it's a bit like an anaesthetic – so that all body sense is numbed. To an Alexander teacher, a drunken student will feel both tense and rather dead at the same time. Because it's very difficult for any input to come through from the teacher's hands, there is not a lot of sense in having a lesson. Similarly, some extreme diets produce extreme muscle contraction as if the whole body were tightening in on itself and reducing the elasticity of the muscle tone. Extreme exercise regimes have a similar effect. Someone who's doing intensive weight-lifting everyday is going to find it harder at first to benefit from an Alexander lesson. Of course I'm talking about extremes here. When someone is starting Alexander lessons, perhaps they shouldn't be indulging in extremes of anything.

SC: **We touched on it earlier, but I must ask if you ever get bored with teaching?**

N: What we do does look incredibly routine and a newly qualified teacher may go through a phase of getting bored and will ask himself: 'How can I tolerate carrying on doing this?' But most of us have found that as you get more sensitive in your teaching and more able to tune in to what's going on in each student, the students come to seem more and more different. Each student is a new pattern, a new puzzle that the teacher has to find a way into. This keeps the teaching process fresh and very interesting. Sometimes you find yourself conducting little experiments. You see, an Alexander teacher is confronted with a circle or chain of fixations and contractions in the student's body which may correspond to certain held patterns at the emotional and mental levels. Everyone has them to some extent. There's no such thing as a perfect person after all. So the teacher is trying to find a way in. You might ask yourself something along the lines of: 'With this student, will we get any more freedom in the neck at the moment? Or is there a possibility that if I can now get his legs to undo a little bit more, then that will get a freeing up in the lower back which might, in turn, allow him to release his neck and allow his head to go out a bit more?' So you might approach the problem this way, but find the student's legs are absolutely rigid and an alternative strategy is required. It might be the case that he will not be able to let his legs go until things undo higher up in his back. So you try that approach.

On another level, the teacher might say to himself: 'This chap has such a peculiar idea of his body being quite separate from himself that he feels that he has to drive his body to excess with exercise and diet in order to control it. Until we find a way to eliminate this attitude towards his body, he won't be able to let go of some of his muscular rigidities.' This would be another hypothesis and while working one might tactfully try to talk about the subject in order to transform the student's ideas. Again, you might find so much resistance that you back off and try to find another way into the problem.

A teacher may be frequently testing out new hypotheses during a lesson, even at the subconscious level. So it is very interesting. But if an Alexander teacher finds after a couple of years that it's all incredibly boring, he might ask himself the question: 'Am I the type of person cut out to be an Alexander teacher after all?' It is possible that just as most Alexander teachers might not be temperamentally suited to the role of chairman of IBM, so an ambitious executive of IBM might not be temperamentally suited to the role of Alexander teacher. Being an Alexander teacher is not the most important thing in life for most people. It should not be seen as the ultimate goal in life for all humanity.

Still, I would say it is deeply satisfying to do something for a living that seems to be of positive benefit to a great many people.

# The Alexander Technique in a Larger Context

## by JOHN NICHOLLS

*The 1986 FM Alexander Memorial Lecture*
*delivered before the Society of Teachers of the Alexander Technique*
*on October 25 1986*

I am going to begin by drawing your attention to the plans shown on page 106. They outline a schema that we're going to talk about this evening.

The chart on page 106 is a map of other things that have been going on during the time that the Alexander Technique has been evolving. We're going to look at this map and see how certain common themes crop up again and again in all these different fields and disciplines. They are the seven themes outlined on page 106. Then we're going to see how the Alexander Technique itself relates to these seven themes.

Before we do that, I should mention that I was looking over this outline the other day in preparation for this talk, and I had a moment of doubt and anxiety about it all. I'd just given a lesson to a new pupil, someone who had come along with a back problem and basically just wanted to get rid of the pain. After the lesson, I came out and was looking at the notes for the talk, and I suddenly felt anxious at the enormous gulf between this grand scheme outlined here and the, in comparison, quite prosaic process of trying to get across the rudiments of inhibition and direction to someone who just wants to alleviate discomfort. In order to reassure myself, I went back and looked at some of F.M.'s own writing, and I found, in a piece written in 1946, shortly after the end of the war and the dropping of the atomic bombs on Hiroshima and Nagasaki, the following passage. Referring to his own work, he says: 'By these means . . . we are enabled in process to bridge the gulf which has for

too long separated subconsciousness and consciousness in the
control of reaction, and at the same time to widen the gulf between
the human and the animal stages of evolution. (This) could change
and improve the basic nature of man's impulsive and instinctive
reactions . . . Man's basic nature has not changed as it should have
done during past centuries in respect of conscious direction of
his use of himself or in regard to his judgement and control in
human relations. Hence on every hand he is faced with the imped-
ing effects of 'emotional gusts' . . . prejudice, jealousy, greed, envy,
hatred and the like. These are the outcome of reactions which ruin
man's chances of establishing such relations in national and
international affairs as could lead to a better understanding
of what is essential to the engendering of peace and goodwill in the
world . . .' (from *Knowing How to Stop*, Chapter 1, by F. M. Alexander, 1946).

Well, that's a very big statement indeed, about F.M.'s view of his
own work and its relevance to the development of better relationships between individuals in society and between nations at the
global level. So, fortified with the knowledge that he himself saw his
work in such a large context, I pressed on trying to outline a way in
which we can see ourselves in a larger context than that to which we
are accustomed in the day-to-day application of our work.

**Tendency to Isolation**

It seems to me that throughout its development there has been a
tendency for the Alexander Technique to be rather isolated from
everything else going on around it. Isolated in order, of course, to
emphasize its uniqueness, and in that process tending to dissociate
itself from anything else with which it might be confused.
Especially, dissociating itself from any of those things that are now
called fringe, or alternative, or New Age, or esoteric, or some such
word.

This is understandable to some extent because, in F.M.'s own
lifetime, people were bound to try to understand what he was doing
by likening it to other things. We all know how difficult it is to
understand this work, so people constantly attempt to understand it
by saying: 'Ah yes, I see. It's a form of physiotherapy; a kind of
osteopathy; some sort of Western yoga; or it's all to do with positive
thinking and mind control.' This must have been going on naturally

hroughout F.M.'s lifetime, and he would equally naturally be insisting on his uniqueness and his difference from any of those other
hings.

Since F.M.'s death, to some extent the same process has carried
on. We have constantly had to define ourselves by separating ourselves off from all those things with which we might be confused.
Hence F. P. Jones, for example, in his writing, stressed that the
Alexander Technique had nothing in common with methods of
relaxation, meditation and mind control – even though we are
actually always talking of muscular release, awareness and conscious control. Does this have nothing to do with relaxation? medi-
ation? mind control?

Now whilst this emphasis on our uniqueness and our consequent
isolation is understandable, it does have certain drawbacks. In
particular, it has the drawback of making us feel that we are just
a terribly small group. There are about 1,000 people in the world at
the moment who claim to teach the Alexander Technique, and
that really is a very small band, struggling in a vast world of indif-
ference.

Another drawback is that isolating ourselves so much has caused
some teachers to feel the need to build up from the practical elements of the Alexander Technique a whole philosophy of life. They
feel that the practical nature of the work needs amplification and
needs some broader philosophy to explain and sustain it. And so
they take the practical elements and perhaps try to build them up
into a grand structure in which inhibition, non-end-gaining, primary control and so on are turned into great philosophical concepts.
Now I know that the Technique has been described as a philosophy
of life reduced to practical procedures, but if we try to expand it back
out from the practical to the philosophical level, it soon begins to
look like a large edifice perched precariously on a very small base.
Concepts such as non-end-gaining, inhibition, direction and primary control need precise grounding in physical use to be of practical value, but they also need to be seen in a broader context to be of
any value philosophically.

## Bifocal Vision

So, I think the time has come to see where we do fit in to the larger
pattern of things that have been going on in the western world
in this century. I suspect that what we are going to

## LIST OF GENERAL THEMES

1. Consciousness becoming conscious of itself and the unconscious/ subconscious.
2. Need to understand and control our reactions.
3. Out of touch with feelings.
4. The integration of the body and mind.
5. Search for natural functioning (non-interference).
6. Search for a central core to integrate the parts, a Centre, Self or 'I'.
7. Renewed interest in 'vital force', bio-energy, Chi, Prana, etc.

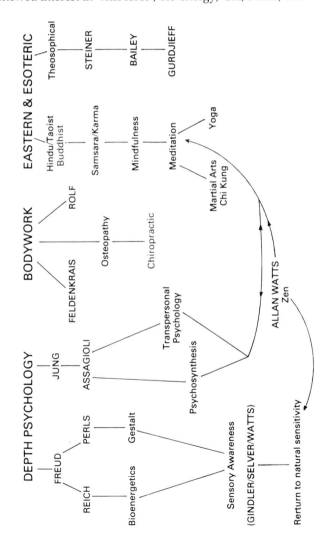

need in the next twenty years or so is a kind of double focus of vision, where we develop more and more the ability to see the broad picture of what we have in common with many other groups of people and disciplines, while retaining also the ability to shift focus down to the precise differences which make us unique. A bifocal vision, like bifocal lenses, in which we can see ourselves as both unique, and also part of a common cause.

## The Map

This map on page 106 is a guide or whistle-stop tour of some of the things I think are important or relevant to us that have been going on during the time the Alexander Technique has been evolving.

You will see that there is no mention of academic science or philosophy on it. Why not? Because the dominant thrust in academic, scientific psychology and academic philosophy has been behaviourist and materialist. I belong to a generation that sat as students in University seminars while intelligent, adult lecturers were paid to persuade us that consciousness was, physiologically, a trivial accident of evolution, something like feedback in an amplified sound system; or, philosophically, an illusion caused by faulty use of language. Since consciousness was regarded by F.M. as Man's Supreme Inheritance, a tradition that has until recently ignored consciousness has not had a lot to say to us except at the detailed level of describing neurophysiological mechanisms.

So, what you have in front of you is a map of some fields that I think are of particular relevance to us, and it is not my aim to explain each of these fields to you tonight. I am assuming that most of you have some acquaintance with some of these things, or if you do not you will know someone who does, and can tell you what to read if you want further knowledge.

My object is to show how, by looking through these different fields, one can extrapolate some common themes, the seven themes in the list on page 106 and then relate the Alexander Technique to them. These seven themes seem to me to crop up again and again in different fields. If we use Jung's terminology, we can view them as new elements arising from the collective unconscious of western culture, little flags popping up and waving, saying, 'Come on, it's time you paid attention to me at this point in your collective development.' Just as in our own individual lives, certain themes and issues come to the fore at particular times, and if we ignore them we may fail to mature fully, we may become lopsided individuals psychologically, so one can, perhaps figuratively, say that within a whole society or culture, different themes come to the fore and need to be dealt with at different times. And speaking of Jung leads straight into:

## Depth Psychology

At the top left of the chart, known as psychoanalysis on the Freud ian side and analytical psychology on the Jungian side. In terms of the themes outlined, depth psychology is dealing with the dis covery of the unconscious, or subconscious (I think for our purpose the two words can be used interchangeably), and therefore with the discovery of consciousness itself as one end of a spectrum.

So here we have the need both to strengthen our consciousness and to investigate the hidden portions of it.

And this has become essential, because during this century it has become more and more obvious that our ability to control ourselves, our own behaviour, has been increasingly outstripped by our ability to control our environment. You will see on the list of themes that this of course is Theme 2 that we are dealing with. It has become a platitude of our times. A line that is trotted out on all great oc casions. F.M. refers to it in the passage I quoted from the essay beginning the little book, *Knowing How to Stop*. Professor John Dewey refers to it in the foreword to *Constructive Conscious Control*. It is usually formulated something like this:

Western science and technology have grown apace and given us tremendous ability to control and change the environment around us and yet there has been no comparable growth in our ability to control our behaviour, or our reactions. This disparity is most graphically shown in how we deal with such an overwhelmingly powerful force as the nuclear bomb. We are in a situation now where weapons that would destroy the whole globe are controlled by a small group of people, yet the control these people have over themselves may not be much more than the control people had over themselves in the days of swords and bows and arrows.

With the development of psychoanalysis from Freud came also the realisation that we are very confused about our own feelings.

Often we really do not know what we feel. Our thoughts and our emotions get terribly confused and at odds with each other. I believe F.M. used to say: 'We don't think half as much as we feel we think.' We are indeed very confused between how we think we ought to feel, and what our feelings actually are. This is Theme 3 – out of touch with our feelings. Often, as a result of work in some form of psychotherapy or counselling, people come to realise that feelings they thought they had were not at all how they really feel. Typical examples are anger and resentment, suppressed and turned into an appearance of caring deeply for the people around you; fear suppressed and turned into aggression against the people around you; and depression, which a person may refuse to recognise and thus become a rather superficial, outwardly cheerful but inwardly isolated character. The private lives of professional comedians sometimes show this. These examples are common currency in individual psychotherapy.

Also in depth psychology is another of our common themes, Theme 7, the vital force or life energy, and we will have more to say about this theme later. (It may be that modern science has made this concept untenable, but it remains as a powerful metaphor that engages the imagination.) Freud called it libido, and saw it as some sort of basic energy, largely sexual. Jung also called it libido, but saw it as something more than just sexual. A life energy. He also termed it psychic energy.

## Reich and Perls

Moving down the chart now to Reich and Perls. Wilhelm Reich, founder of Reichian psychotherapy, vegetotherapy, orgone therapy, progenitor of bioenergetics and neo-Reichian therapy. A tremendously important figure in showing us the connection to the physical body of our emotional states and psychological attitudes. The body as a map of the unconscious. The musculature as an expression of the psyche. Reich's term for it was muscular armouring. Reading the body as a way into the mind. Working with the body as a way of bringing these things into awareness and hence having greater control of them. Fritz Perls, founder of Gestalt therapy, had a way of observing unconscious gestures and mannerisms, for example, and using them as a key to what the body was expressing, and how that showed the hidden motivations behind our outward verbal and conscious expression. So Theme 4 comes in here. Integration of body and mind. Working with the one to affect the other.

Also, here, Theme 7. Reich became more and more interested in libido as a physical reality he called bio-energy, or orgone energy. He believed he could prove its existence in laboratory science. That has certainly been much disputed, but it is useful to know that he said the flow of this life energy could be blocked by the muscular tensions associated with psychological conflict, and this damming up of energy could eventually result in disease.

Both Reich and Perls derived the basics of their approach to psychology from Freud, and so Themes 1, 2 and 3, which we have already looked at in connection with psychoanalysis, would be taken for granted by these two men.

## Sensory Awareness Training

Moving on down the left hand side of the chart, the names of Gindler and Selver are names that will not be known to most of you, but I put them in because they were very influential in America in the development of Humanistic Psychology, particularly via the Essalen Institute. They very clearly exemplify another of our common themes.

Elsa Gindler was a German lady who had TB and set about trying to cure herself. She succeeded in doing this by examining her own way of breathing, and bringing about improvements in it that eventually cured the TB. In the process, she felt that she had removed unnatural interferences subconsciously imposed on her breathing and got back to something that could be called 'natural breathing'. Following on her success in this and the TB clearing up, she got on to the idea that all of us in a civilised society seem to greatly interfere with the natural working of all sorts of physiological functions. We interfere with our posture, balance, movement, and with the way we use our senses: sight, hearing, touch, even taste and smell; and, of course, the kinaesthetic sense. So she began running workshops in which she taught exercises to help people get back in touch with natural functioning. Trying to remove the accretions and distortions that civilised living seems to put on the way we use our bodies. Hence Theme 5 here – the search for natural functioning or non-interference.

Elsa Gindler trained a lady called Charlotte Selver, who went to America and there met Alan Watts, whom we will come on to a bit later, but who was a very influential teacher and philosopher. He wrote a great deal about eastern mysticism and western psychology and he introduced Charlotte Selver to the Essalen Institute in California, where she gave her classes in Sensory Awareness Training. These classes had a great influence on some of the people who were developing Humanistic Psychology including Fritz Perls and Erich Fromm.

# Jung

Returning now to the top of the chart, still under Depth Psychology, we will look at the strand that passes through Jung. In Jung we find a more positive approach to the unconscious or subconscious than we find in the Freudian writings. In Jung there is an emphasis that the unconscious is not just a bag of repressed drives and instincts, which would run amok if not controlled, but Jung stressed that within the psyche as a whole, taking the conscious and unconscious together, there is a fundamental drive towards wholeness, a fundamental drive towards balance, towards harmonisation. In every individual, if in their way of life they are becoming more and more unbalanced, their own nature will, unconsciously if necessary, lead them into circumstances that may jolt them back into balance. Your own psyche will create patterns that will try to bring you back into harmony.

Self-balancing, self-healing, self-realisation. Individuation – Jung's own word for this process when it is developed consciously. Further on down that strand on the map there is Roberto Assagioli, who many of you will know as the founder of Psychosynthesis. Here also is Transpersonal Psychology – which is like a combination of Jung and Assagioli with the concepts of a few others like Abraham Maslow thrown in.

The interesting thing here for us is Assagioli's concept of sub-personalities. This refers to the fact that we all seem to have different aspects of ourselves that cause us to behave almost like a different person in different situations. You know how a man can be one person at home with his wife and family, a quite different person an hour later at work, and another different person again over a drink with friends in the evening.

It is as if we all go around driving in a mini-bus with half a dozen or more characters who keep knocking each other out of the driving seat and taking over the wheel for a bit. In order to get more control over ourselves, we need to find some central core, some sort of I, or centre, or self, which will integrate these fragmentary sub-personalities in ourselves and choose who is going to take the wheel at any given time. Which takes us to the last of our common themes, Theme 6, the search for a central core to integrate the parts. A centre, self, or I. Trying to get ourselves centred. A good expression to indicate a state of calm, of balance, and of integration.

## Bodywork

Leaving that part of the map, we go up to the top and into the middle. I've put the label, 'Bodywork'. It is only a label to indicate specifically body-oriented disciplines.

Osteopathy and chiropractic are the most widely known and influential of these. It is quite curious how they both arose in the U.S.A. at about the same time. In the latter part of the nineteenth century, both D. D. Palmer and Andrew Taylor Still seem to have come up independently with very similar ideas, perhaps responding to a collective need in the same way that Freud and Jung seemed to be doing.

How do they fit in to our pattern of common themes? Well, clearly Theme 4 – integration of body and mind. We may think of chiropractors and osteopaths as being very mechanical and structural in their approach, but the writing of the early pioneers suggests an awareness of the human being as an organic whole, body and mind together. Emotional, psychological, spiritual states, all interrelating with the physical state.

Here we find a link with Themes 5 and 7. Quite commonly now, the rationale of a modern osteopath is to say something like this: 'I am working on the spine to bring into balance the sympathetic nervous system which is very easily disturbed at its outlets from the spinal cord, and so by working on aligning and balancing the spine, I am aligning and balancing the nervous system and alleviating disturbances in the natural functioning of the organism. (Theme 5) This will also contribute to the free flow of vital energy through the body and aid self-healing processes.' Theme 7, and also Theme 6, crop up here. The spine itself is seen as central in both these disciplines. It is what integrates, influences for better or worse every aspect of the organism's functioning.

Off on two side-shoots on this part of the map we have:

## Rolf and Feldenkrais

You will all know these two. Relevant points for us are: the body as the way into the psyche. Reading the body as the key to the unconscious. Working on the body as the key to reorganizing elements at other levels – emotional, intellectual and so on. All the things that come under the heading of Theme 4.

So leaving the bodywork field, and skipping on across to the heading:

## Eastern Religions

I have put this in because I think eastern thought is becoming an important influence in the western world. The first influential thinker to show any signs of influence of eastern ideas was probably Schopenhauer back in the 19th century. But in the last 20 years more and more people have come into contact with Hindu, Buddhist and Taoist ideas. Indeed, I woke up one morning last week to hear, on Radio 4, The Dean of King's College, London telling us about Chinese, Taoist philosophy. There are a lot of popular books on the subject. In particular, books such as *The Tao of Physics* and *The Dancing Wu Li Masters*, which emphasize parallels between eastern ideas and some of the most recent developments in modern western science.

Moving on down this line, I have written two Sanskrit words: Samsara and Karma. I have written them because they exemplify the eastern approach to Themes 1 and 2 in our list of common themes. Theme 1 – consciousness becoming conscious of itself and the unconscious, and Theme 2 – the need to understand and control our reactions.

Samsara is the word to describe the chain of events that keep us going from one lifetime to another. Karma is the law of cause and effect. The way in which our past actions determine our future circumstances. Usually this is seen in terms of reincarnation, but the same thing applies within one lifetime. Our reactions in one situation being the cause of the next situation. Action and reaction. Cause and effect. There is a sense in the eastern writing on this subject of being driven by unconscious urges, being bound, as they say, on the wheel of Samsara, the wheel that carries us from one existence to the next and from one life situation to the next inexorably. This sense is very much akin to that expressed in Themes 1 and 2 and exemplified in depth psychology. The sense that we are driven by unconscious desires and have little control of ourselves. Can we get off the wheel of Samsara was the burning question of the Buddha. Can we free ourselves from unconscious compulsions?

Eastern religions are rich in practical methods for helping people to free themselves. One of the key methods is what is called in Buddhist discipline Mindfulness. Mindfulness simply means trying to be more conscious, more aware of ourselves here and now as we are acting and reacting with each other. It is one of the key practical techniques for dealing with the problems of Themes 1 and 2.

## Meditation

Mindfulness in daily life is also brought to a precise focus in the specific activity of meditation. Of course many different meditation methods have been developed in the East, and it is remarkable how in the last ten years they have become more and more accepted in the western world.

What is meditation? It is an enormous subject and one into which we cannot go deeply tonight. A few aspects relevant to our attempt to extrapolate common themes are: meditation as quietening the mind to reach deeper levels – consciousness immersing itself in the unconscious (Theme 1). Meditation as quietening the nervous system to restore natural functioning. This is emphasized by TM practitioners. They say that regular practice of meditation dissipates layers of disharmony we have put on top of the proper functioning of the nervous system (Theme 5).

Non-interference is especially apparent in the Zen tradition, which in turn brings in Alan Watts who was a prolific writer interpreting Zen to the west, so it is appropriate that he should have the link to Charlotte Selver and Sensory Awareness Training. Non-interference is particularly emphasized in one Zen school where it is said that just sitting is meditating. The sitting is the meditation. There are also walking meditations and just walking is meditating. While we are on this subject, everyone who has ever read any Zen literature has a favourite Zen story and can rarely resist the compulsion to tell it, so here is mine. It is very short. It concerns the master who said: 'When you sit, just sit. When you stand, just stand. When you walk, just walk. Above all, don't wobble'

Wobbling in this context could be defined as conflict between two different activities trying to go on at the same time. In this kind of meditation, our aim would be to quieten everything down until only absolutely essential activity is happening in the body. In other words, in our Alexander jargon, inhibiting all unnecessary doing. It is said that if you can achieve that you will come into contact with your true nature. (Theme 5 – search for natural functioning)

Moving on down to the last branch of the eastern part of the chart we have the techniques of:

## The Martial Arts and Yoga

Some of these psychophysical disciplines are now very common and popular in the west. Under the martial arts I have put Chi-Kung (or Qi Gong in the more recent spelling) which may not be so familiar to you. I have put it because chi (or qi), as many of you will know, is the Chinese word for life energy, vital energy. And Chi-Kung is the art of learning to develop and circulate consciously that energy. It is a system of meditations, internal exercises, postures and movements which can be practised as a part of a martial art discipline or it can be practised for its own sake.

So, Theme 7 – renewed interest in vital force, bio-energy, chi. Looking at this in the context of the martial arts and Chi-Kung, we see the importance of physical alignment and muscular release to facilitate the flow of energy. A Chinese Tai Chi teacher I used to go to always spoke of the spine as a central channel. He used to say 'Be an open channel for your chi,' as the aim of what he was trying to teach. Here again, Theme 6. Within the chi disciplines, the spine seems to be the central channel that integrates all the energy flows.

In yoga, of course, we have practices concerned with the circulation of prana – prana being the Sanskrit which means much the same thing as the Chinese chi. Again the emphasis is on physical alignment and freedom, and the central function of the spine itself.

Moving over now to the far right hand side of the chart and the section headed Esoteric, I should more accurately call that:

## Modern Western Esoteric Teaching

One could roughly say that the first big influence in this area was Helena Blavatsky and the Theosophical Society, which is why I have put it in there, but it is there purely as a historical reference point.

Out of it came two figures that are of interest to us- Rudolf Steiner and Alice Bailey, but I want first to jump to the bottom of that line on the map and look at Gurdjieff.

## Gurdjieff

He was a teacher of Russian origins, who came out of the Sufi tradition of the Middle East. He is particularly interesting to us, because more than anyone else in this whole schema he emphasized the fragile and fleeting nature of human consciousness.Gurdjieff used to say that everyone is asleep, everyone walks about in a state of waking sleep. We assume that because we fall asleep at night and then wake up in the morning, we are then conscious; and we easily delude ourselves in this way because if somebody comes up and says 'Are you conscious?' we immediately wake up out of this state of waking sleep and say 'Yes, of course I am ' and straight afterwards we fall asleep again. So here we have Theme 1 again. Gurdjieff also emphasized stopping our automatic reactions. He actually taught an exercise called the Stop exercise. He would say that, because we are half asleep, we go through our lives like automatons, acting and reacting on automatic pilot. Much of the Gurdjieff work to wake us up is also to help us stop reacting mindlessly and begin to make real choices in the way we behave – Theme 2 . Theme 4 crops up here also, as Gurdjieff work involves a lot of body-awareness training through special movements and manual labour. In fact, Gurdjieff is quoted as saying: 'Thus a man can never get away from his repertory of intellectual and emotional postures until his moving postures are changed.' (From *Views from the Real World* Arkana 1973, p. 156.) Also strongly evident here is Theme 6. Gurdjieff talked of the need to find our Real I, that centre in ourselves from which we could regain control over the fragmentary parts of ourselves.

## Steiner and Bailey

Going back now to Rudolf Steiner and Alice Bailey, their work is a little more difficult to fit into this scheme of things and to assimilate to our work as Alexander teachers. But within the Steiner and Bailey writings there is a lot of interesting and suggestive material about subtle energy flows and the chakra system. I will just throw in a few points that you might keep at the back of your mind when considering the broader significance of our own work.

In both these teachings it is said that a human being is basically an energy transformer and that our purpose here on earth is to take in energies from the world around us, process them through the lower chakras or centres which are in the lower part of the body and raise the energy up to the heart and the head, the heart and the head symbolising the higher levels of feeling and higher levels of thinking that human beings are capable of. It is stressed that it is only safe and sensible to do this, to raise energies up to the heart and the head, when we are well grounded, that is when the lower centres, the lower half of the body, are properly functioning.

We are told that energy is to be raised up through the spine to open the heart and to light the lamp of consciousness in the head. Lighting the one Light, the one Light because consciousness is common to us all. In all of this it is interesting to consider what may be the role of the neck and the back. The back must be free and open to let energy rise through the spine, and the neck above all must be free, free to allow energy to pass up from below to sustain the light of consciousness, and free to allow that light to pass back down again and so to enlighten the lower centres of the body. Actually, Themes 1, 2, 5, 6 and 7 all crop up in esoteric work, but that is enough now on the items on the chart.

## The Role of the Alexander Technique

To come back now to the Alexander Technique and its tendency to seem isolated from everything else. We want at this point to look at how the Alexander Technique relates to these seven themes that we have seen come up again and again in modern consciousness. I think that what the Alexander Technique has to contribute to this broader scheme of things is something essentially very practical. It is a very precise tool for putting into practice the ideals of these larger movements. We are not here as Alexander teachers to present a grand philosophy to people – there is plenty of grand philosophy in all these other things – but we can offer a precise and practical tool literally to embody, to bring into the physical body and everyday life, ideas and ideals expressed in these other fields. So to look at our work in the context of the seven themes, we will go through them quickly one by one and see what we can contribute.

*Theme 1*　Consciousness becoming conscious of itself and the unconscious or subconscious

Well, it is pretty clear how we relate to that. 'The conscious mind must be quickened' – that is a quote from F.M.A. 'Man's Supreme Inheritance' – the title of one of his books. He defined our Supreme Inheritance as our ability to develop conscious guidance and control. And from that book, there's a very nice little quote:

'Returning to my definition of the subconscious self, it will be seen that I regard it as a manifestation of the partly-conscious vital essence, functioning at times very vividly, but on the whole incompletely, and from this it follows that our endeavours should be directed to perfecting the self-consciousness of the vital essence.' (*Man's Supreme Inheritance* by F.M.A., p. 25, 1957 edition.)

That quote seems very interesting in the light of all the themes we are talking about here tonight. The vital essence becoming more conscious of itself.

*Theme 2*　The need to understand and control our reactions

Very obviously, Inhibition. The practical application of inhibition. Teaching people that you do have a choice. You can actually choose here and now not to react in the way you have been programmed to react up until now. Incidentally, quite by chance I recently came across the following quote about inhibition:

'One of the dangers of our civilisation is . . . that one function of the nervous system, which is to prompt to action, to excite, should grow out of all proportion to another function, which is to inhibit, to control, to enforce rest.' – From *The Biology of the Seasons* by Prof. J. A. Thompson, 1911.

Professor Thompson also uses the picturesque analogy of modern man having a steam engine in his brain that pounds along relentlessly at full speed. This steam engine has a safety valve that shunts steam through a whistle when too much pressure has built up. However, in our way of life we have developed the dangerous ability, with distractions and drugs, to ignore the whistle that is telling us it is time for inhibition, time to damp down the pressure. Instead, the engine races on until it self-destructs.

That was written in 1911, one year after the first publication of *Man's Supreme Inheritance*. Professor Thompson, as far as I know, had no connection with F.M. An interesting example of these ideas being in the air at that time.

*Theme 3*   Being out of touch with our feelings

This I think relates closely to faulty sensory appreciation. I know that we use that to refer to kinaesthetic perceptions, to say that our feedback from our bodies has become unreliable. But some important schools of modern psychology, particularly stemming from the Reichian tradition, would suggest that those people who are very out of touch with their own bodies are likely to be very cut off from their feelings And a distorted body image is likely to go with emotional reactions that are continually out of proportion to the immediate situation. Alexander Lowen's books give a good insight into this.

*Theme 4*   Integration of body and mind

There is nothing much to say about this except that while it is often taken for granted these days, F.M. was truly one of the great modern pioneers in insisting on psycho-physical unity. Psycho-physical integration. Treating the bodymind as a unit.

*Theme 5*   The search for natural functioning (non-interference)

What we refer to as non-doing could be described as removing interferences with the essential activity of the organism.

In practical terms, as I am standing here, I need to inhibit any unnecessary efforts to hold myself up artificially, I need to direct to facilitate the natural working of those muscles and other parts that do have to operate to keep me up against gravity, and I have to release the considerable tensions caused by the stress of standing up here talking to all of you! By getting the natural balance of the head and spine working, I will also be helping my breathing, circulation and digestion, all my life support systems to function naturally.

The stripping away of non-essential activity in order to allow natural functioning is obviously an important part of our work.

*Theme 6*   The search for a central core to integrate the parts, a Centre, Self or 'I'

Well, the Primary Control. The primary control is indeed that relationship within our body that integrates the various parts of the body. It integrates us on a physical and neurophysiological level. And, mysteriously, it also seems to help us feel more integrated psychologically when we have this primary balance working in ourselves. In most of us in modern society, these two aspects, thinking and feeling, get very much out of joint, out of harmony.

The good functioning of the primary control (head/neck/bac balance) is probably an indicator of someone's state of being an health, both physically and psychologically.

It may also be an indicator of the degree to which the person i able to act authentically, to behave and communicate from thei deepest self.

*Theme 7* Renewed interest in vital force, life energy, bioenergy, etc.

Now this is a tricky one, but I would say that the way we talk abou Direction within the Alexander Technique has links to this theme. I is a tricky one because some Alexander teachers are extremel attracted to this way of thinking and some are extremely put off b it, and would prefer that we didn't discuss such things at all, or us such terms.

In this respect I was fascinated to discover that in September magazine called *The Journal of Alternative Medicine* published it description of a disagreement between two leading organization representing Complementary and Alternative Medicine in thi country. One, the Institute of Complementary Medicine, says th following:

'The philosophy of all the natural therapies depends on an ar preciation of the so-called 'life energies'. When the energy is inter rupted, a series of problems occurs which may potentially result in lessening of well-being or produce the symptoms of disease. Th natural therapies attempt, by individual methods to restore th natural flow of life energy by removing the causes of thes problems, The practitioner's ability to understand the condition o the 'life energies' is therefore crucial to the success of the treatment. (*Journal of Alternative Medicine*, September 1986.)

According to the Journal, the other organization, the Council fo Complementary and Alternative Medicine, says nothing publicl about such things and seems to feel it would be best not to discus such things in public. So we are not the only people to feel divide on this subject.

A useful way to help bridge this division is to treat descriptions o energy flows in the body as descriptions of subjective phenomena In other words, when the Chinese sages of many centuries ag practised their Taoist meditations and chi-raising exercises, they al experienced feelings that they described as energy flowing throug channels in the body. Whether or not such energy and such channels exist objectively does not alter the fact that enough people experienced the same feelings to pass descriptions of them down through the generations.

We complain sometimes about the inadequacy of language to describe kinaesthetic sensations, so we could usefully consider descriptions of vital energies, chi or prana, as extensions of kinaesthetic language, new ways of describing internal sensations. We might say, 'It feels as if energy is flowing from here to here', without having to ascribe objective reality to it. Certainly, in casual conversation Alexander Technique teachers have a tendency to refer to direction as if it were an energy flow. We speak of a teacher having 'very strong direction' or 'lots of direction'. And teachers talk of an upward flow through the spinal column.

In the Tai Chi Classics (the traditional writings describing Tai Chi Chuan) it is said that you must direct your movements by mind intent, not by muscular force, then you will develop chi or vital energy. It seems to me that that is not a bad description of direction without doing in our terms.

## Conclusion

That concludes our tour through the psychophysical spectrum. I think it is a valid and worthwhile exercise to look at the broader context of what has been going on around us, extrapolate common themes, and see how we relate to them. I hope you found it worthwhile, too. I would just remind you at the end, as I did at the beginning, that we need to view all this with bifocal lenses. To see with the distance lens how much we have in common with activities and pursuits that many thousands of people have been involved in throughout this century – you might call it the evolution of consciousness in the physical body – but to see also with the close-up lens how we have a unique, precise and practical contribution to make to that larger context.

## Postscript

After this lecture I was asked where I would put the Alexander Technique on the chart on page 106. On reflection, it seems to me that the Technique is the window through which we as Alexander teachers may view the whole chart. Anyone working in one of the other disciplines mentioned here could prepare a similar lecture and a similar map, removing his own discipline and finding a place for us on the map. His own discipline would be the window through which he sees the larger context.